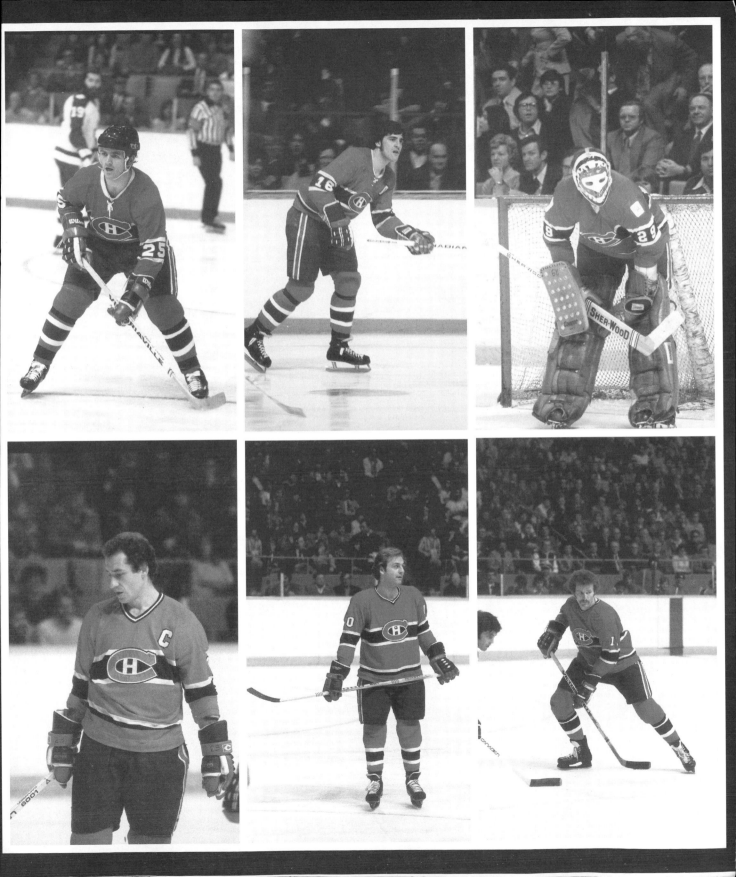

Between them (left to right) Jean Beliveau (10), Bernie Geoffrion (6) and Henri Richard (11) won 27 Stanley Cups as members of the Montreal Canadiens.

Previous page (clockwise from top right): Jacques Lemaire, Serge Savard, Ken Dryden, Bob Gainey, Guy Lafleur, Larry Robinson.

Mike Leonetti

The Montreal Canadiens Trivia Book

1909–2005

The Montreal Canadiens Trivia Book, 1909–2005
© 2005 by Mike Leonetti. All rights reserved.

Published by Collins, an imprint of HarperCollins Publishers Ltd

First edition

HarperCollins books may be purchased for educational, business
or sales promotional use through our Special Markets Department.

HarperCollins Publishers Ltd
2 Bloor Street East, 20th Floor
Toronto, Ontario, Canada
M4W 1A8

www.harpercollins.ca

Library and Archives Canada Cataloguing in Publication

Leonetti, Mike, 1958–
The Montreal Canadiens trivia book, 1909–2005 /
Mike Leonetti. – 1st ed.

ISBN-13: 978-0-00-639548-5
ISBN-10: 0-00-639548-1

1. Montreal Canadiens (Hockey team) – Miscellanea. I. Title.

GV848.M6L46 2005   796.962'64'0971428   C2005-901675-2

HC 9 8 7 6 5 4 3 2 1

Printed and bound in the United States
Set in Minion and Eras

The first edition of this book
is dedicated to two great voices
of the Montreal Canadiens,
Danny Gallivan and Dick Irvin.

Danny Gallivan

Dick Irvin

Acknowledgements

The works of the following writers were used to help put this book together: Stan Fischler, Chris Goyens, Dick Irvin, Liam Maguire, Brian McFarlane, Claude Mouton, Allan Andy O'Brien, Andrew Podneiks and Allan Turowetz.

The trivia books by the following authors were an invaluable source of information and inspiration for many of the questions in this book: Kerry Banks, Dan Diamond (editor), Don Weekes, Ron Wight and Eric Zweig.

Newspapers I consulted: *The Hockey News, The Globe and Mail, The Montreal Gazette.*

Sources for statistics and records: *The NHL Guide and Record Book* (various issues), *Total NHL* (2003 edition), *Total Hockey* (2nd edition), Montreal Canadiens media guides (various issues), *Stanley Cup Playoffs Fact Guide* (various issues).

Photographs provided by:
   Harold Barkley Archives
   Dennis Miles
   National Archives of Canada
   Robert Shaver
   York University Archives
   Molson Sports and Entertainment
   Hockey Hall of Fame, from the following archives:
      James Rice
      Imperial Oil–Turofsky
      Graphic Artists
      Doug Machellan
      Paul Bereswill

Contents

Saku Koivu earned his first All-Star appearance in 1998, and finished with 57 points in 69 games.

Introduction

Montreal Canadiens Moments

It has been said that playing for the Montreal Canadiens has a certain mystique about it. Put on the *bleu, blanc et rouge* and something special happens to the player who finds the famous CH logo on his sweater. This is never more the case than during the Stanley Cup playoffs, when the Habs become the fiercest competitors on ice. There is plenty of history to illustrate the point amply—just examine the performance of the Canadiens when the greatest prize in sports is on the line.

Take, for example, the 1966 finals, when the Canadiens lost the first two games of the series on home ice to the Detroit Red Wings. The Motowners made the mistake of thinking they had the Cup in the bag, and the proud Habs got wind of the Red Wing arrogance. During the next four games Detroit barely touched the puck as the Habs swatted the Red Wings away without much

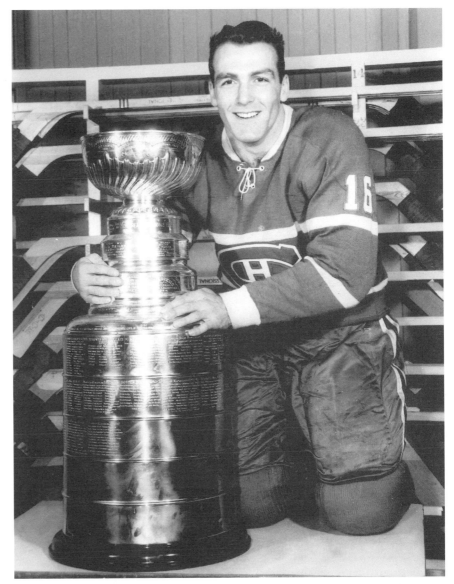

Henri Richard played in 180 playoff games for Montreal scoring 49 goals and 80 assists.

difficulty. The series ended on a controversial note when Henri Richard scored an overtime winner that should not have counted, but it would not have mattered. The Canadiens would have scored another goal or won game seven on home ice. Coach Toe Blake and his players had been challenged and there was no way Detroit was getting the Cup—end of story! The Canadiens' win in this series was the first time this author witnessed the Habs' intense drive in the playoffs, and it was something that made a long-lasting impression on a young hockey fan.

If someone needs more convincing, take a look at the 1971 playoffs that saw the underdog Canadiens win another Stanley Cup. The Boston Bruins were supposed to run them out of the rink in the opening round. Some rookie netminder named Ken Dryden was to be the lamb being fed to the slaughter, but the tall goalie could actually stop the puck. His teammates seemed to catch on to the idea that the record-breaking Bruins could be defeated. The comeback from a 5–1 second period deficit in the second game of the series was a Canadiens classic (winning 7–5), and their 4–2 win right in Boston in game seven stunned the hockey world. It looked like the Habs were in even deeper trouble when they were down 2–0 in the seventh game of the final against Chicago in '71. Suddenly, Jacques Lemaire scored a goal from about 65 feet out and the Habs were back in it! The "Pocket Rocket" then went to work and potted two to clinch the Cup once again with a 3–2 win at the Chicago Stadium.

Or how about the 1986 playoffs when the Canadiens were again led by a rookie netminder, Patrick Roy? The team was loaded with rookies but that did not seem important as the '86 post-season wore on. An overtime goal (the earliest ever in NHL history) in the second game of the finals against Calgary seemed to change the tide of the series, and the sensational goaltending of Roy

gave the Canadiens a surprise championship. If the '86 title was unexpected, then what can be said about the 1993 team? Ten straight overtime wins put the Habs in position to win their 24th Stanley Cup, highlighted by their three OT wins versus the Los Angeles Kings in the finals. The first of these victories came in the second game of the final at home where the Habs were down 1–0 in the series and losing 2–1 late in the contest. The goalie was pulled and a keen eye caught an illegal stick being used by the Kings, giving the Habs a couple of extra skaters. Not only did the Canadiens tie it up, they won it in overtime, and the Kings never recovered. The sportscasters on CNN said it was the "ghosts of the Montreal Forum" that did in Los Angeles that night but really it was just part of a long history of excellence which has most often seen the Habs skate off with the Stanley Cup as *Hockey Night in Canada* rolls the credits to end another season.

Even in the 2004 playoffs the Montreal mystique was still alive (if just for a brief period of time). The Habs had never been down 3–1 in a playoff series, but they came back to edge out Boston in seven games to advance to the next round. It looked like the Habs were all done after they had lost the fourth game of the series at home to a devastating overtime goal. There was even some backbiting in the Habs dressing room after the tough defeat, but they rallied as only the Canadiens can and beat the Bruins three straight (twice in Boston) to win the series. Players like Jose Theodore, Michael Ryder, Richard Zednik and Sheldon Souray seemed to understand that playing for Montreal in the post-season is indeed special!

The Habs have an incredible history of winning with a style and grace that makes them the envy of all other hockey teams. The Habs dynasty teams have had some of the greatest players in NHL history as their backbone—including the likes of

Howie Morenz, Maurice Richard, Jean Beliveau, Jacques Plante, Doug Harvey, Henri Richard, Ken Dryden, Yvan Cournoyer, Larry Robinson, Guy Lafleur, Serge Savard, Bob Gainey and Patrick Roy, to name a few—with a superb supporting cast that would star on many other teams. The Canadiens have played many of hockey's greatest games and this book is a tribute to those moments and players that have thrilled hockey fans from coast to coast in Canada and the United States.

This first edition of the *Montreal Canadiens Trivia Book* is filled with many great moments such as those mentioned above. Each chapter looks at the team from a different angle: memorable games, records and awards, trades, names

from the past, plus other interesting facts. The answers to the trivia questions are at the end of each chapter. A variety of photos will remind you of the great games and names associated with the Canadiens.

The book was put together from a wide variety of sources—newspapers, game programs, media guides, NHL fact and statistical guides, television and radio broadcasts, magazines and many books. Every attempt has been made to ensure that all of the information is accurate. Any errors are those of the author. Hab fans have traditionally been very demanding, and it is my hope that their high standards have been met in this book.

Enjoy this look at hockey's greatest franchise!

Jose Theodore has already defeated the Boston Bruins twice in the playoffs.

Yvan Cournoyer had a great playoff year in 1973.

Memorable Games

1) The Montreal Canadiens played their first-ever game, as members of the National Hockey Association (NHA), on January 5, 1910. Their opponent was a team from Ontario. Can you name the opposition and the player who scored the first goal in Canadiens history?

2) What was unusual about the location of the Canadiens' first contest?

Georges Vezina won 175 games for the Canadiens between 1910 and 1926.

3) The Canadiens first played for the Stanley Cup in 1916, when they faced the Portland Rosebuds in the finals. All the games were played in Montreal, and for the first time in Cup play, the best-of-five series went the distance. The Canadiens won the Cup with a 2–1 win on March 30, 1916. A little-used defenceman scored the winning goal. Can you name him?

4) The Montreal Canadiens played their first National Hockey League contest on December 19, 1917. Who were the opponents, and which Montreal player scored five goals in the game?

5) He was the first great goaltender in the history of the NHL, so it was only fitting that he recorded the first shutout in league history when the Canadiens blanked the Toronto Arenas 9–0 on February 18, 1918. Can you name the goaltender?

6) By 1919 the Canadiens were back in the Stanley Cup finals, playing against the Seattle Metropolitans. The series, which was played exclusively in Seattle, was called after five games, at which point each team had won twice, with one game ending in a tie. Why was the series called? The reason for the cancellation was also responsible for the death of a Habs player on April 5, 1919. Who was he?

7) The Canadiens opened a new rink on January 10, 1920, when they played their first game at the Mount Royal Arena. What team did the Habs beat 14–7, and which Montreal player scored six times in the contest?

8) A March 3, 1920, contest saw the Canadiens set an NHL goal-scoring record that has not been surpassed since. What is the record that they set that night?

9) On their way to winning the 1924 Stanley Cup, the Canadiens beat three Canadian-based teams in the playoffs to win the championship. Can you name all three clubs?

10) On March 22, 1924, this impressive Montreal rookie recorded a hat trick to give the Habs the lead in the Stanley Cup finals. Three days later, he scored the Cup-winning marker. Can you name the smallish centre who scored these important goals?

11) The Canadiens were not supposed to open the Montreal Forum (which was built to house the Montreal Maroons), but an electrical problem at their own home rink, the Mount Royal Arena, forced the Habs into the change of venue. Who scored the first goal in the new building, and what team did the Habs beat on the night of November 29, 1924?

12) After playing in a remarkable 325 consecutive games for the Canadiens, this goaltender was forced to leave the team's home (and season) opener against Pittsburgh on November 28, 1925. He was diagnosed with tuberculosis and died a few months later. A trophy was donated by the team in his memory, to be awarded to the goalie on the team allowing

Howie Morenz scored 256 career goals as a Hab.

the fewest goals against during the season. Can you name the goalie and the trophy?

13) The Montreal Forum became the permanent home of the Canadiens beginning with the 1926–27 season. The Habs played their first "official" home game at the Forum on November 18, 1926. Who was the opposition, and what was the final score?

14) A playoff game on March 28, 1930, saw the Canadiens battle the New York Rangers at the Forum. The score was knotted at 1–1 at the end of regulation time, and it took 68 minutes and 52 seconds of overtime before the game was decided in the Habs' favour. A little-known, light-scoring right winger (he notched only four goals in 88 career games) ended the longest overtime game in Canadiens history. Can you name him?

15) Boston was the best team in the NHL during the 1930–31 schedule with a 38–5–1 record. They beat the Montreal Canadiens four times during the regular season. However, in the best-of-three Stanley Cup finals, the Habs swept the Bruins in two straight games, including a Cup-clinching 4–3 win at the Forum on April 3, 1930. Who scored the winning goal for Montreal?
Hint: He was known as "The Stratford Streak."

16) In 1931, the Canadiens became the second team in NHL history to win back-to-back Stanley Cups. The best-of-five final featured two overtime contests—both won by Chicago—but the Habs came through with a road win in the decid-ing game on April 5, 1931, blanking the Blackhawks 2–0. Who scored the winning goal, and who earned the shutout?

17) The biggest star in the early days of hockey was the legendary Howie Morenz. Though he also played for Chicago and the New York Rangers, he spent the majority of his career in a Canadiens uniform—including his final NHL game, in which he suffered a broken leg, on January 28, 1937. He died a short time later in hospital.

To aid his family, the Canadiens held a benefit game in his memory at the Forum on November 3, 1937. In that game, players from the Canadiens and Montreal Maroons combined to form one team, which played against a roster of NHL all-stars. Who won the contest, and how much money was raised?

18) Albert "Babe" Siebert was set to take over as coach of the Montreal Canadiens for the 1939–40 season, but he drowned in the summer of '39. The Canadiens held a benefit game to raise funds for his family. The contest was held at the Forum on October 29, 1939. Who won the game between the

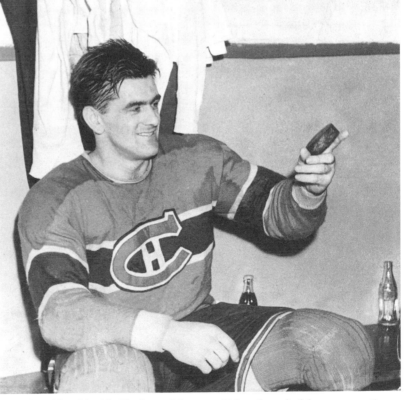

Maurice Richard (#9) holds the puck he scored his 45th goal of the season to tie Joe Malone's single season record during the 1944–45 campaign.

Montreal's famed "Punch Line" (left to right): Maurice Richard, Elmer Lach and Hector "Toe" Blake.

Canadiens and the NHL All-Stars, and how much money was raised?

19) Maurice "Rocket" Richard first became known as a clutch post-season performer during the 1944 playoffs. The flashy Montreal right winger acquitted himself very well in the second game of the semi-finals, played at the Forum against the Toronto Maple Leafs on March 23, 1944. In that game, he accomplished something no other player had done to that point. What was his feat, and how was it recognized after the game?

20) Fans attending the fourth game of the finals between Montreal and Chicago on April 13, 1944, were expecting the Habs to complete a sweep of the Blackhawks on home ice. But the 'Hawks were not going to give up easily; they forced Montreal to rally furiously just to tie the score and send the game into overtime. After 9:12 of extra play the Habs scored the winner, ending a 13-year Cup drought. Who scored the all-important goal?

21) One of the best games Maurice Richard ever played in his illustrious career came on December 28, 1944, when he scored five goals

and added three assists in a 9–1 romp over the Detroit Red Wings. Who was the Detroit goalie that night at the Forum, and what had Richard been doing earlier in the day that made this feat even more remarkable?

22) Scoring 50 goals in 50 games was a monumental exploit when Maurice Richard did it during the 1944–45 regular season. His final goal of the season came on March 18, 1945, in a road game against the Bruins, and it set a new standard for all hockey players to strive for. Which Bruins goalie gave up the Rocket's historic tally?

23) Maurice "The Rocket" Richard was the first player to set a record by collecting four points (three goals, one assist) in one period of an NHL playoff game. He set the mark in the third period of a semi-final contest at the Forum on March 29, 1945. Who did the Habs beat, and which Canadien was the first of many players to tie the record?

24) After knocking off the Chicago Blackhawks in the opening round of the 1946 playoffs, the Habs faced the Boston Bruins in the finals. Although the Canadiens won the Stanley Cup in five games, three of the contests went into overtime (two of them were won by Montreal). In the last game, played on

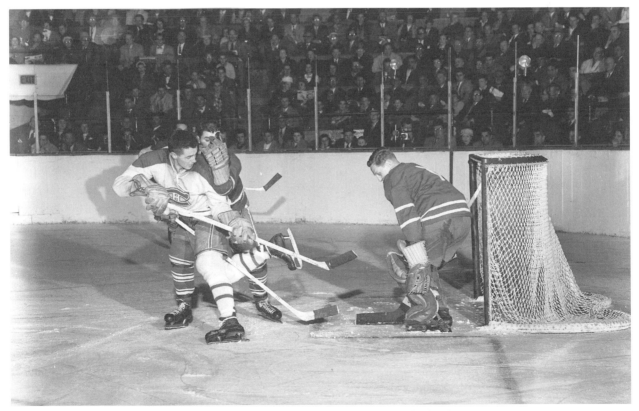

Jean Beliveau is all tied up in front of the Toronto Maple Leaf net occupied by Ed Chadwick.

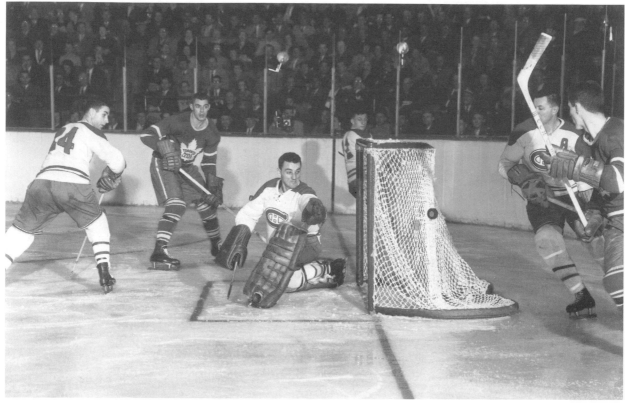

Goaltender Jacques Plante without the face mask in the late 1950s.

April 9, 1946, at the Forum, one Hab had a goal and two assists to help Montreal earn a 6–3 win. Who was the star of the clinching contest?

25) The longest playoff game the Canadiens have ever played on the road occurred on March 27, 1951, at the Detroit Olympia. The Habs needed 61:09 of overtime to win the first game of the semi-final series against the Red Wings 3–2. Who scored the winner?

26) The 1951 Stanley Cup finals were unique in that every game of the series went into overtime. The Canadiens won only one of those overtime contests (at Maple Leaf Gardens on April 14), while the Toronto Maple Leafs

took the other four. On April 21 at the Gardens, the Maple Leafs won the Stanley Cup on the best-known goal in club history. Who scored the lone game-winning goal for Montreal, and who scored the Cup-winning goal for Toronto?

27) On October 11, 1952, the Montreal Canadiens defeated the Detroit Red Wings 2–1 at the Forum. What was significant about that contest?

28) A semi-conscious Maurice Richard returned to the Canadiens bench late in the third period of a playoff game against the Boston Bruins on April 8, 1952. It was the seventh game of their semi-final series, and the score

was tied, 1–1. Richard had been crunched by a pair of Bruins earlier in the game, but somehow managed to return to the ice. Never one to shy away from drama, Richard took the puck the length of the ice before scoring the winning goal in a game that ended 3–1. Richard's marker sent the Canadiens to the Stanley Cup finals (where they would be swept by Detroit). Which Boston goalie allowed Richard's most famous goal?

29) A November 8, 1952, contest between the Canadiens and Blackhawks saw Maurice Richard reach a significant scoring milestone before the hometown fans. What was the new mark Richard established, and which Chicago goaltender gave up the goal?

30) Montreal coach Dick Irvin was somewhat desperate on the night of April 4, 1953. His team trailed Chicago 3 games to 2 in the semi-final series; if they failed to win game six, they would be eliminated. He decided to make a goaltending change, benching veteran Gerry McNeil and inserting a rookie who had never played in an NHL playoff game. The move paid off as the Habs won the game 3–0 and took the series in seven games. Who was the goalie Irvin turned to for the key contest?

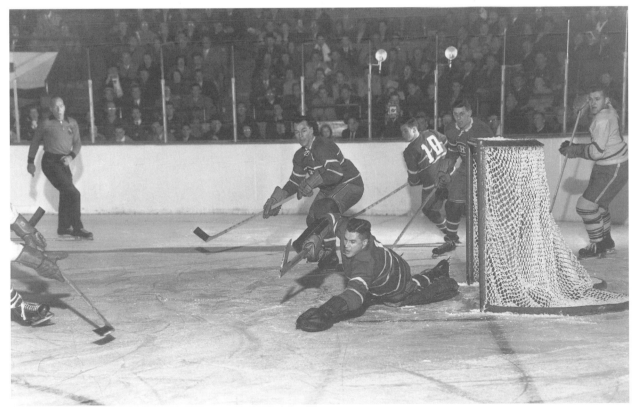

Goaltender Gerry McNeil (#1) pounces on a loose puck.

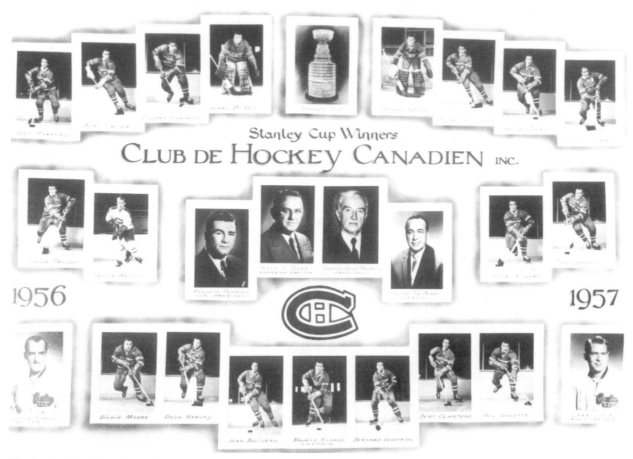

Stanley Cup Winners

CLUB DE HOCKEY CANADIEN INC.

1956

1957

The Stanley Cup champions of 1956–57

31) On April 16, 1953, the Canadiens won the Stanley Cup at the Forum with a 1–0 overtime victory over the Boston Bruins in the fifth game of the finals. Who played goal for Montreal, and who scored the overtime winner? Also, something unusual happened to the goal scorer. Can you recall what it was?

32) The Montreal Forum hosted the NHL's first annual All-Star Game on October 3, 1953. The Canadiens, as defending Stanley Cup champions, took on a team of stars drawn from the other five teams. What was the result of the game, and which rookie signed his first contract with the Habs on the same day?

33) Montreal and Detroit easily advanced to the Stanley Cup finals in 1954—the Canadiens disposing of Boston in four straight while Detroit needed only five games to knock off the Toronto Maple Leafs. The finals would prove to be a memorable battle. Montreal fell behind 3 games to 1 before winning the next two games by scores of 1–0 and 4–1. That sent the teams back to Detroit for a decisive seventh game on April 16, 1954. A very close contest was decided in overtime by a fluke

goal: a shoot-in bounced off the glove of a Habs defenceman and into the net past Gerry McNeil for a 2–1 Red Wings win. Who scored the goal for Detroit, and which Canadiens blueliner had the puck bounce into his own net as he tried to play the puck?

34) The 1954–55 season saw Montreal's Bernie Geoffrion win his first Art Ross Trophy as the NHL's top point producer (38 goals and 37 assists for 75 points). On February 19, 1955, he pumped in five goals during a 10–2 romp against the New York Rangers at the Forum. Which goalie allowed all five goals?
Hint: This netminder would later play for the Canadiens.

35) Maurice Richard was one of the most closely checked players in NHL history, and it frustrated him at times. He was known for losing his cool, and on the night of March 13, 1955, he went a little too far, taking out his anger on the Boston Bruins—and a linesman (Cliff Thompson) who tried to restrain him. His violent response to a check—which had left him bloodied—cost Richard dearly: NHL president Clarence Campbell suspended him for the rest of the season and the play-

offs. Oddly enough, the Bruin who upset the Rocket so much that night was a former teammate. Can you name him?

36) March 17, 1955, will live forever as the night the Richard Riot broke out in the streets of Montreal. Canadiens fans let the world know about their displeasure with their best player and hero being sidelined for the rest of the regular season and playoffs. They were especially rough on Clarence Campbell, who decided to attend the game that night at the Forum. The contest was never completed; a tear-gas bomb sent people scrambling for the exits, and the Habs were forced to forfeit the game to their opponents—whom they were chasing for first place. What team gained the

New coach Toe Blake talks strategy with players Maurice Richard (left) and Jean Beliveau.

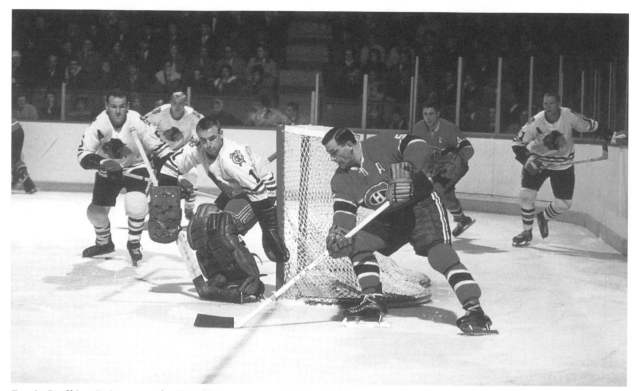

Bernie Geoffrion (#5) was one the Canadiens top scorers during the '50s and early '60s.

benefit of the forfeiture, and how did the rioting finally stop?

37) A November 5, 1955, contest at the Montreal Forum saw one Canadien score three power-play goals in 44 seconds while the Boston Bruins were down two men. The NHL decided to make a rule change as a result of the hat trick. Who scored the goals, and what rule change did his outburst inspire?

38) Toe Blake's first game in the Stanley Cup finals as coach of the Habs was played on March 31, 1956, at the Forum. Going into the third period, the situation looked bleak for Montreal, who trailed 4–2. But a four-goal period propelled the Canadiens to victory,

and they ultimately won the Cup in five games. Who scored the four goals, and which team did Montreal gain a measure of revenge against in the '56 finals?

39) On April 10, 1956, the Canadiens clinched the Stanley Cup with a 3–1 home-ice victory. They were led by a player who scored a goal and added two assists. His goal gave him a total of seven in the finals, setting a new modern-day mark that has been equalled only twice since. Can you name the Habs player, as well as the others who tied his record?

40) October 30, 1957, saw Maurice Richard reach another significant NHL milestone when he scored his 500th career goal during a game at

the Forum. Which future Hall of Fame netminder gave up the goal?

41) Montreal won its second Stanley Cup in a row by knocking off the Boston Bruins in five games during the 1957 finals. The Canadiens got off to a great start in the opening game, played on April 6, 1957. Maurice Richard scored four goals, including three in the second period, to give the Habs a 5–1 victory. How many times did Richard score three goals in one period of a playoff game during his career?

42) The Boston Bruins gave the Canadiens a much harder battle in the 1958 Stanley Cup finals than they had in '57. The teams split the first four games, and the fifth, played at the Forum on April 17, 1958, was tied 2–2 at the end of 60 minutes. The Habs scored the winner at 5:45 of extra time. Who scored this important goal, and what made it even more significant?

43) The Canadiens equalled an NHL record first set by the Toronto Maple Leafs when they took their third straight Stanley Cup, defeating the Bruins at Boston Garden on the night of April 20, 1958. They took the final contest by a 5–3 score, paced by the two-goal performance of a player who also notched the Cup winner. Can you name him?

44) Montreal played Chicago in the semi-finals in 1959, and although they won the series in six games, it ended controversially. The sixth game was played in Chicago on the night of April 4, 1959. On a play in the third period, Al Langlois supposedly tripped Bobby Hull. The referee did not call a penalty

against the Canadiens, who came back down the ice and scored the winner to secure a 5–4 victory. Enraged Blackhawks fans tried to attack the official, but he was rescued by one of the Montreal players. Who was the referee, and which Canadien came to his aid?

45) On their way to a fourth consecutive Stanley Cup in 1959, the Canadiens got a great playoff performance from an unexpected source. This winger had scored only 13 goals during the 1958–59 regular season, but racked up 10 markers in the post-season, including the Cup clincher during the fifth game of the series, played April 18, 1959, at the Forum. Can you name the player?

46) A game at New York's Madison Square Garden on the night of November 1, 1959, proved to be historic. It was during that game that Canadiens goalie Jacques Plante

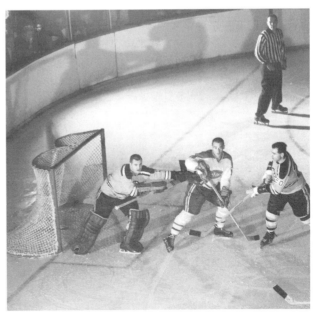

Montreal forward Marcel Bonin is caught between Boston goalie Don Head and defenceman Leo Boivin.

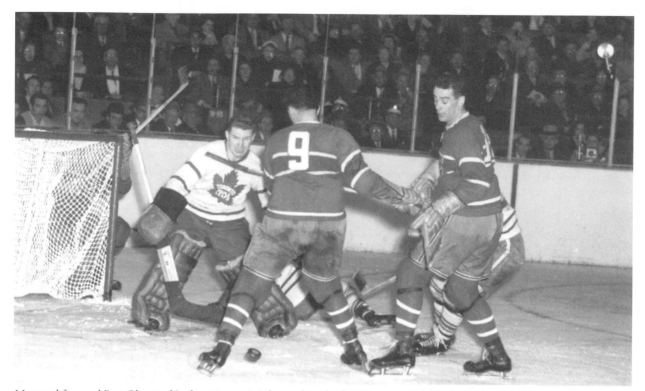

Montreal forward Bert Olmstead is about to swat at the puck at the feet of teammate Maurice Richard (#9).

first donned a face mask in a regular-season contest. His face was badly cut when one of the Ranger players deliberately struck Plante in the face with a rising shot. Plante was stitched up, but he vowed he would only return to the game if allowed to shield his battered face. When coach Toe Blake relented, hockey history was made, and the Habs went on to win 3–1. Which Ranger took the shot, and why did he want to hit Plante in the face with his drive?

47) Even though Montreal netminder Jacques Plante lost 3–1 to the New York Rangers on the night of March 20, 1960, at Madison Square Garden, he still won something very significant for the fifth consecutive season.

What did Plante win, and how was he able to do it despite the loss?

48) Although this Montreal defenceman was primarily known as a playmaker rather than a goal scorer, he did manage to score one playoff overtime marker. It came at the Forum on March 26, 1960, during the second game of the semi-finals between Montreal and Chicago. The goal served to redeem the blueliner, who had been directly responsible for the Blackhawks knotting the game at 3–3. Can you name him?

49) In the 1960 finals, the Canadiens had no trouble knocking off Toronto for the second straight year: they swept the Leafs to claim

their fifth consecutive Stanley Cup. In the third game of the series, played at Maple Leaf Gardens on April 12, Maurice Richard scored the 82nd and final playoff goal of his career. Which Leafs goalie gave up the Rocket's last goal, and how many of Richard's 82 playoff goals were scored in the finals?

50) Montreal whipped Toronto 4–0 on the night of April 14, 1960, to win their fifth consecutive Stanley Cup, a streak no other team has been able to match. What other mark did Montreal equal that same night with their win at Maple Leaf Gardens?

51) The night of March 16, 1961, was an interesting one at the Forum. Two players were vying for their 50th goal of the season, which would equal the standard set by Maurice Richard. The Canadiens sniper hit the mark, while the member of the visiting Maple Leafs did not. Can you name the successful Hab, the Leaf who came up just short and the Toronto netminder who allowed the milestone goal?

52) A semi-final playoff series between Montreal and Chicago signalled the end of the Canadiens dynasty in 1961, but not without controversy. The third game of the series was played in Chicago on March 26, and the Habs needed a goal by Henri Richard in the last minute of regulation time to tie the game at 1–1 and force overtime. In the third extra period, a penalty to Dickie Moore of the Habs gave Chicago the chance to score on the power play, and they did. The Blackhawks went on to win the series in six games. Who scored the winning goal for the 'Hawks in game three, and what did the Canadiens coach do as soon as the game was over?

53) In the entire decade of the 1960s, only one player scored five goals in a single game. It happened at the Forum on February 1, 1964, as the Canadiens beat the Detroit Red Wings 9–3. Which Montreal player scored the five goals, and which goalie allowed them all?

54) Between 1961 and 1964 the Canadiens were unable to advance beyond the first round of the playoffs. They felt they had a good chance when they finished first in the 1963–64 regular season, which pitted them against the third-place Maple Leafs in the semi-finals.

Henri Richard (#16) scored many big playoff goals over his illustrious career.

Defenceman Doug Harvey (left) has a chat with Maurice Richard.

Montreal took a 3–2 series lead, but Toronto came back to win the next two games, including a 3–1 triumph in game seven at the Forum on April 9, 1964. One Leaf scored all three Toronto goals. Can you name him?

55) After losing to the Maple Leafs in the playoffs for two straight years, the Canadiens got their revenge on April 13, 1965, and they did it at Maple Leaf Gardens. Montreal led the semi-final series, 3 games to 2. The Leafs took an early lead in the sixth game, but the Habs forced overtime and won the game 4–3, with a goal in the first overtime period. Who scored the goal that put Montreal into the finals for the first time since 1960?

56) It took seven games, but the Canadiens defeated Chicago to take the Stanley Cup in 1965. The final game of the series was played on May 1 at the Forum, and it was over quickly. Just 14 seconds into the game, the Habs stormed the Blackhawks zone and scored. They cruised to an easy 4–0 win. Who scored the opening goal? Also, which

Hab was the first winner of the Conn Smythe Trophy as playoff MVP?

57) Detroit shocked the hockey world by beating Montreal twice on Forum ice to open the 1966 Stanley Cup finals. The Canadiens recovered and won the next four contests to retain the Cup. The sixth game of the series was played at the Olympia on May 5, and the game was settled in overtime on a goal that should not have counted because it was batted in with an arm. But there were no video goal judges in those days. Referee Frank Udvari allowed the goal to stand, giving the Canadiens a 3–2 win and the Cup. Who scored the debatable goal for Montreal?

58) In 1966–67 the All-Star Game was moved from early October (just before the season began) to mid-season. In the game, played at the Forum on January 18, 1967, two Montreal goalies combined to shut out the NHL All-Stars 3–0. Can you name the two netminders who recorded this All-Star Game first?

59) The New York Rangers were a much-improved team in 1966–67 and made the playoffs for the first time since 1962. However, the Canadiens were too powerful for the young Rangers, whom they quickly dispensed with in four straight games. The last game of the series was played on April 13, 1967, at Madison Square Garden and was won 2–1 in overtime by Montreal. Who scored the goal that got the Habs back into the finals in the last year of the "Original Six"?

60) Montreal was supposed to beat the Maple Leafs easily in the 1967 finals. Plans were made for the Stanley Cup to be displayed at Expo 67. The Habs got off to a great start, winning the opener at home on April 20, largely on the efforts of one player who scored three goals in the contest. Who recorded the hat trick, and how did the series turn out?

61) The 1967–68 season, the first of the expansion era, saw the Canadiens claim the Stanley Cup once again when they completed a sweep of the St. Louis Blues with a home-ice victory on May 11, 1968. Which Montreal defence-man scored the Cup-winning goal in a 3–2

Goaltender Charlie Hodge makes a save against Bob Pulford of the Maple Leafs.

J.C. Tremblay (left) was an excellent rushing defenceman.

triumph, and what was significant about this contest from a coaching point of view?

Who scored the goal, and who was in the Bruins net?

62) The toughest series the Canadiens played en route to capturing the 1969 Stanley Cup was in the semi-finals against the Boston Bruins. The first two games featured Montreal coming from behind to win in overtime (on goals by Ralph Backstrom and Mickey Redmond), but the Bruins evened the series on home ice. After taking the fifth game at home, the Canadiens went into Boston on the night of April 24, 1969, hoping to wrap up the series. The game went into double overtime before this Montreal player scored the only overtime winner of his career.

63) In 1970, the Montreal Canadiens missed the playoffs for the first time since 1948 after finishing fifth in the East Division. The Habs actually tied the New York Rangers in points (92); the deadlock was to be broken based on total goals scored, and the Rangers ended up leading that category, 246–244. The Rangers boosted their total with a 9–5 win over Detroit on the last day of the season. The Canadiens went into their final game on April 5, 1970, knowing they had to score at least five times to beat the Rangers for the playoff berth, but they only scored twice,

dropping a 10–2 decision. Which team beat the Canadiens, and how is it that they managed to score so many goals in such an important game?

64) Nobody expected the Montreal Canadiens to beat the powerful Boston Bruins in the opening round of the 1971 playoffs, especially with a rookie netminder named Ken Dryden. The Habs lost the first game 3–1 and were about to lose the second contest, played at the Boston Garden on April 8, 1971. They were trailing 5–1 when, at 15:33 of the second period, they got a goal back. In the third stanza they added five more goals (two from Jean Beliveau and one each from John Ferguson, Jacques

Centre Jacques Lemaire (#25) was one of the most underrated performers when he played in the NHL.

Lemaire and Peter Mahovlich) to win the game 7–5. The game seemed to turn the tide for the Canadiens. Who scored the late-second-period goal that got the Habs rolling?

65) Montreal and Chicago staged one of the greatest Stanley Cup finals in 1971. The seventh and deciding game was played in Chicago on April 18. The Habs were trailing 2–0 and looked to be in trouble when a blast from centre ice found its way past a shocked Tony Esposito in the Blackhawks net. The goal revived the Canadiens and they rallied, on the strength of a pair of goals by Henri Richard, to win the contest 3–2. Who scored the goal from 65 feet out?

66) The Canadiens and Blackhawks met once again in the 1973 Stanley Cup finals, and as expected the Habs took the series in six games. The final game was played in Chicago on May 10, 1973, and featured a two-goal performance (including the Cup-clinching tally) by the eventual winner of the Conn Smythe Trophy. Which player scored the goals and took the coveted award as the best performer in the playoffs?

67) One of five NHL players to score five goals in a game during the the '70s, this Canadien enjoyed his great night on February 15, 1975, in front of the hometown fans. Montreal whipped Chicago 12–3, and one netminder gave up all the goals to the Hab with the hot stick. Can you name the Montreal player and the goalie he beat five times?

68) Hockey fans around the world will always remember New Year's Eve, 1975, when the Canadiens hosted the Soviet Red Army team

Winger Steve Shutt (#22) had a Hall of Fame career with the Canadiens.

at the Forum. The much-anticipated contest saw the Habs dominate, but it ended in a 3–3 tie. Vladislav Tretiak was superb in the Russian net, while Ken Dryden faced only 13 shots from the Soviets. Who scored the Montreal goals?

69) One of the best things to happen in the history of hockey was Montreal's tearing apart of the Broad Street Bullies from Philadelphia in the 1976 Stanley Cup finals. Montreal won the first two games at home by 4–3 and 2–1 scores, then won the third contest 3–2. The last game of the series was played at the Spectrum on May 16, 1976, and the Flyers were no match for the high-flying Habs, who won the contest 5–3. Who scored the winning goal for the Canadiens?

70) Montreal faced the Boston Bruins in the 1977 Stanley Cup finals, and the series was really no contest as the Habs swept their long-standing rival. The Bruins did force overtime in the fourth and final game, played in Boston on May 14, but the Canadiens dashed their hopes of extending the series when they scored after 4:32 of extra play. Who scored the Cup-winning goal?

71) Montreal easily made it to the Stanley Cup finals in 1978, losing only one game (to Detroit) before meeting the Boston Bruins for the championship. The Bruins were much more determined this time, and they won two games before the Canadiens took the series in six games. Montreal won its third straight Cup on May 25, 1978, by beating Boston 4–1 at the Garden. Who scored the Cup-clinching goal?
Hint: He would later go on to coach the Habs.

72) One of the greatest playoff hockey games in history was played at the Forum on May 10, 1979. It was the seventh game of the semi-final series between Montreal and Boston. The Habs trailed for most of the game, but they sent it into extra time when they scored a late power-play goal (after the Bruins had been assessed a two-minute minor for too many men on the ice!). The Canadiens dominated in overtime and won the contest to advance to the finals. Who scored the goal to even the game, and who got the winner in overtime?

73) Even though the New York Rangers won the first game of the 1979 Stanley Cup finals, the Canadiens bounced back to win the next four to take their fourth consecutive championship. On May 19 at Madison Square Garden, the Habs solidified their hold on the series when they won the fourth game 4–3 in overtime to take a 3–1 series lead. Who scored the overtime winner?

74) The Minnesota North Stars ended Montreal's four-year hold on the Stanley Cup when they beat the Canadiens on April 27, 1980, in the seventh game of a quarter-final playoff series. It was a close contest that was not decided until late in the third period, when the Stars scored, stunning the Forum crowd. Who scored the go-ahead goal to give Minnesota a 3–2 win?

75) The Montreal Canadiens and Quebec Nordiques developed a fierce rivalry after the Nords joined the NHL in 1979. It was especially intense during the playoffs, and the Nordiques enjoyed a couple of overtime post-season victories that came right in the Forum and eliminated the Habs. The first occurred on April 13, 1982, during a best-of-five division semi-final, and the other came on May 2, 1985, during a seven-game division final. Who scored the series-winning goals for the Nordiques?

76) Rookie goaltender Patrick Roy was outstanding during the 1986 playoffs, which ended in another Stanley Cup for the Canadiens. His best performance came on the night of May 5 at Madison Square Garden in New York, when Roy stoned the Rangers in overtime. Once the Canadiens got out of their own end they scored a goal to take the game 4–3, giving them a 3–0 lead in a series they would win in five games. Another rookie scored the overtime winner for Montreal. Can you name him?

77) The Los Angeles Kings walked into the Montreal Forum and won the first game of the 1993 Stanley Cup finals. They almost won the second game on June 3, 1993, but the Habs rallied late to even the series. A Kings player was found to be using an illegal stick, putting the Habs on the power play. The Canadiens pulled their goalie, giving them

Guy Lafleur (#10) is the Canadiens leader for career points (1,246).

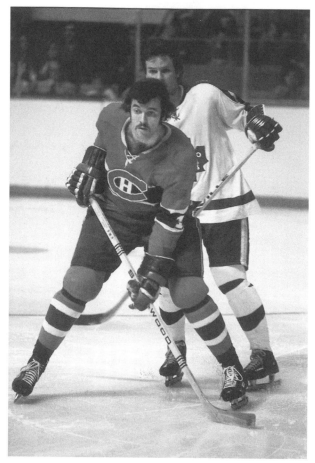

Yvon Lambert (#11) scored 181 goals in 606 games for the Canadiens.

yet another extra skater. The strategy worked, as Montreal got a goal from a defenceman—his second of the night—to even the game at 2–2. The same player scored in overtime to win the game, making him the first defenceman to record a hat trick during a final series. Can you name him?

78) March 11, 1996, was a sad night in many ways, as the Montreal Forum hosted its last NHL game. Who provided the opposition, what was the final score and which Hab scored the last goal at the fabled arena? Also, which

Canadiens alum received the longest, loudest and most emotionally rousing ovation when introduced?

79) The Canadiens made a return to the playoffs in 2002 and beat the heavily favoured Boston Bruins in six games in the opening round. Against Carolina in the second round, they were about to pull ahead 3 games to 1 on the night of May 9, 2002, but they lost a 3–0 lead in the third period and the Hurricanes scored in overtime to win the game 4–3 at the Bell Centre. Carolina went on to beat Montreal in six games. Which Hurricane scored the overtime winner in the fourth game of the series?

80) Montreal had never trailed a best-of-seven playoff series by 3 games to 1, but that is where the Canadiens found themselves during the opening round of the 2004 play-offs against the Boston Bruins. A pair of 5–1 wins evened the series, and the seventh game was played on May 19, 2004, at the FleetCenter. The Habs completed their comeback with a 2–0 win and once again defeated the Bruins in the post-season. Who got the shutout, and which player scored the winning goal?

Answers

1) Montreal beat the Cobalt Silver Kings, 7–6, in overtime. Newsy Lalonde scored the first goal for Montreal.

2) It was played on a natural ice surface at the Jubilee Rink. An estimated 3,000 spectators were in attendance.

3) Goldie Prodgers scored the winner. He played in 24 regular-season games in his lone season with the Habs.

4) Montreal defeated Ottawa 7–4. Joe Malone scored five times.

5) Georges Vezina

6) The finals were halted due to an influenza epidemic. Many players were stricken, and the Canadiens were unable to ice a full team. Montreal defenceman Joe Hall died of the disease just five days after the last game was played.

7) Montreal defeated the Toronto St. Pats in the game, and Newsy Lalonde scored six times for the Canadiens.

Defenceman "Bad" Joe Hall twice led the NHL in penalty minutes.

Maurice "Rocket" Richard beats "Sugar" Jim Henry of the Bruins for his most well-known goal.

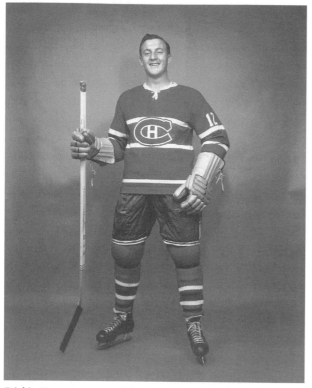

Dickie Moore was one of the most determined players ever to wear the Habs sweater.

8) The Canadiens set a record for most goals in one game with 16. They defeated the Quebec Bulldogs 16–3.

9) Montreal knocked off the Ottawa Senators (NHL), Vancouver Millionaires (PCHA) and Calgary Tigers (WHL) to take their second Cup.

10) Howie Morenz

11) Billy Boucher scored the first goal just 56 seconds into that inaugural contest, helping his Canadiens beat the Toronto St. Pats 7–1.

12) Georges Vezina was the durable goaltender, and the award was named the Vezina Trophy. Beginning in 1982, the criteria for the award were changed; it is now presented to the goalie judged—by the general managers of all NHL teams—to be the best in the league.

13) The visiting Ottawa Senators defeated the Canadiens 2–1.

14) Gus Rivers, who played on the Cup-winning Habs teams of 1930 and 1931

15) Howie Morenz

Jean Beliveau (#4) celebrates winning the Stanley Cup in 1965.

16) Johnny Gagnon scored the winning goal, and George Hainsworth earned the shutout.

17) The All-Stars beat the Montrealers 6–5. The Morenz family received close to $20,000 from all sources.

18) The All-Stars beat the Canadiens 5–2, and $15,000 was given to Siebert's family.

19) Richard scored five goals in a 5–1 win over Toronto, and when the three stars of the game were announced, he was named as the first, second *and* third stars.

20) Hector "Toe" Blake

21) Rookie netminder Harry Lumley was in the Red Wings net. Richard had spent the afternoon moving furniture from his apartment to his new home!

Yvan Cournoyer (#12) was known as the "Roadrunner" because of his great speed.

Mario Tremblay played and coached for the Montreal Canadiens.

22) Harvey Bennett

23) Montreal beat Toronto 10–3. They went on to lose the series in six games. Dickie Moore tied the record on March 25, 1954, when he had two goals and two assists in the first period of a playoff game against Boston.

24) Elmer Lach

25) Maurice Richard

26) Maurice Richard scored the only winning goal for Montreal, while defenceman Bill Barilko scored the Cup-clinching marker for Toronto.

27) It marked the first time a hockey game was broadcast on national television in Canada. It was also the first televised game for the Habs' legendary broadcaster Danny Gallivan.

28) "Sugar" Jim Henry

29) Richard became the NHL's all-time goal-scoring leader with his 325th career goal, surpassing the

Serge Savard was steady performer for the Canadiens between 1966 and 1981.

record set by Nels Stewart. Al Rollins was in the Chicago net.

30) Jacques Plante

31) Gerry McNeil was in goal for the Habs, and Elmer Lach scored the winning goal. Lach had his nose broken during the celebration of the goal!

32) The All-Stars beat the Canadiens 3–1. Jean Beliveau signed his first NHL contract on the day of the game and drew an assist on the Montreal's only goal, scored by Maurice Richard.

33) Tony Leswick scored for Detroit, while Doug Harvey was the unlucky Hab.

34) Lorne "Gump" Worsley

35) Hal Laycoe, who played with the Montreal Canadiens between 1947–48 and 1950–51

36) Detroit was awarded the contest, by a 4–1 margin (the score at the time the game was stopped). It was a significant win: the Red Wings took first place in the final regular-season standings by two points. Maurice Richard went on the radio to plead with the fans to stop the unrest. He also appealed to the fans to get behind the Canadiens for the playoffs.

37) Jean Beliveau scored the goals and was assisted on all three by Bert Olmstead. The NHL adopted a new rule whereby a player serving a minor (two-minute) penalty would be allowed to return to the ice once the opposition scored a goal.

38) Montreal got goals from Jackie Leclair, Claude Provost, Bernie Geoffrion and Jean Beliveau to beat Detroit 6–4.

39) Jean Beliveau set the mark, which was matched by Mike Bossy (in 1982) and Wayne Gretzky (in 1985).

Claude Lemieux was known as a super pest during his NHL career.

40) Glenn Hall of the Chicago Blackhawks

41) Three times

42) Maurice Richard netted the winner, and it was the last of his record six overtime play-off winners. Only Joe Sakic of the Colorado Avalanche has scored as many playoff overtime goals.

43) Bernie Geoffrion

44) Red Storey was the referee, and Doug Harvey is the Montreal player who protected him from the unruly fans. When NHL president Clarence Campbell questioned Storey's judgment after the game, Storey resigned and never officiated another game.

45) Marcel Bonin

46) Andy Bathgate took the shot, and he targeted Plante because the Habs netminder had sent him sprawling into the boards earlier in the game when the two were chasing a loose puck.

47) Plante won his fifth straight Vezina Trophy. That same night, Chicago netminder Glenn Hall allowed five goals in a game against Boston. Plante therefore took the Vezina because his team had allowed two fewer goals (178) than Chicago (180).

48) Doug Harvey

49) Johnny Bower was the netminder. Richard's 34 goals in the finals are still an NHL record.

50) By sweeping both Chicago (in the semi-finals) and Toronto, the Habs matched the achievement of the 1952 Detroit Red Wings by winning the Stanley Cup in eight straight games.

51) Bernie Geoffrion ended the season with 50 goals, while Frank Mahovlich failed to score, leaving him at 48 for the season. Cesare Maniago was in the Leafs goal. Montreal won the game 5–2.

Eric Desjardins (#28) was a big performer for Montreal during the 1993 playoffs.

52) Murray Balfour scored the winner after 52 minutes and 12 seconds of overtime. Habs coach Toe Blake rushed out onto the ice and punched referee Dalton McArthur, earning himself a $2,000 fine from NHL president Clarence Campbell.

53) Bobby Rousseau scored all five goals against Red Wings netminder Roger Crozier.

54) Dave Keon

55) Claude Provost

56) Jean Beliveau scored the goal and also won the Conn Smythe Trophy.

57) Henri Richard

58) Charlie Hodge and Gary Bauman

59) John Ferguson

60) Henri Richard scored three times in that first game, but Toronto won the Cup in six games.

61) J.C. Tremblay scored the winner in the third period. It was Toe Blake's final game as coach of the Canadiens.

62) Jean Beliveau scored his goal against Gerry Cheevers of the Bruins.

63) Chicago beat the visiting Canadiens. Their offence was helped by the Habs' decision to pull their goalie

in the second period in a desperate attempt to score the goals they needed. The Blackhawks scored five times into the empty Montreal net.

64) Henri Richard
65) Jacques Lemaire
66) Yvan Cournoyer
67) Yvan Cournoyer scored all five of his goals against Mike Veisor.
68) Steve Shutt, Yvon Lambert and Yvan Cournoyer
69) Guy Lafleur
70) Jacques Lemaire
71) Mario Tremblay

72) Guy Lafleur scored to tie the game, while Yvon Lambert scored the overtime goal to win the game 5–4.
73) Serge Savard
74) Al MacAdam
75) Dale Hunter in 1982 and Peter Stastny in 1985
76) Claude Lemieux
77) Eric Desjardins. Montreal went on to win the Stanley Cup in five games.
78) Montreal beat the Dallas Stars 4–1, and Andrei Kovalenko scored the final goal at the Forum. Maurice Richard got a 10-minute standing ovation when he was introduced to the Forum crowd.
79) Niclas Wallin
80) Jose Theodore blanked the Bruins, while Richard Zednik scored the winner.

Goaltender Jose Theodore shines during the playoffs, as shown by his post-season play in 2002 and 2004.

Records and Awards

1) This Montreal player set an NHL record (which has since been equalled only four times) by scoring five goals in one playoff game when the Canadiens beat the Ottawa Senators 6–3 on March 1, 1919. Who was he?

2) The first playoff game–winning overtime goal the Montreal Canadiens scored after joining the NHL came during the 1919 Stanley Cup finals versus Seattle. It was in the last game of the series (which was not completed due to an outbreak of influenza) on March 30, 1919. Who scored the goal for the Habs?
Hint: His brother also played on the team.

3) Two Montreal defencemen have scored four goals in one game. It happened for the first time on March 3, 1920, during a 16–3 win over the Quebec Bulldogs, while the other occasion was a 10–6 win over the Hamilton Tigers on January 14, 1922. Can you name both blueliners?
Hint: Both defencemen are in the Hall of Fame.

4) This Hall of Fame netminder holds the NHL record for most shutouts in one season (22, in 1928–29). He also holds the playoff mark for the longest shutout streak (270 minutes, 8 seconds) during the 1930 postseason. Who was he?

5) Which goaltender holds the Canadiens team record for most career shutouts: Jacques Plante, Bill Durnan, Ken Dryden or George Hainsworth?

6) The first Montreal Canadien to take a penalty shot (he was stopped by George Hainsworth of Toronto in a 2–1 loss on November 10,

Newsy Lalonde scored 37 goals for the Canadiens in 1919–20.

Goaltender George Hainsworth played in 318 career games for the Canadiens.

1934) was also the first to score a penalty-shot goal for the Habs (he scored against Andy Aitkenhead of the New York Rangers in a 5–3 win on December 4, 1934). Can you name him?

Hint: He was a member of Montreal's Stanley Cup–winning teams of 1930 and 1931.

7) He was the first player to record five assists in a playoff game when the Canadiens beat the Toronto Maple Leafs 5–1 on March 23, 1944. His performance set an NHL record that was equalled by several players but was not surpassed until 1982 (the record is now six). Who was the Montreal player who first set the mark?

8) A rookie left winger with the Habs set an NHL record by scoring three goals in his first NHL game on January 14, 1943, in a 5–1 win over Chicago (only one other player has scored three goals in his NHL debut). Can you name the player who had the big night for Montreal?

Hint: He would play in only eight career games for the Habs.

9) Buddy O'Connor was the first Montreal player to record four assists in one period (the third) when the Canadiens beat the New York Rangers 10–4 on November 8, 1942. On December 29, 1962, a Montreal defenceman equalled the mark with four assists in the second period of a 5–1 win over the Detroit Red Wings at the Forum. (The current NHL record is five, held by Dale Hawerchuk.) Which blueliner tied the team record that night?

10) Which Montreal centre was the first NHL player to record six assists in one game when the Habs beat Boston 8–3 on February 6, 1943?
Hint: This player was the first Montreal Canadien to win the Art Ross Trophy (in 1948).

11) This player became the first Montreal goaltender to face a penalty shot during the playoffs. In the fourth game of the Stanley Cup finals on April 13, 1944, the netminder stopped Virgil Johnson of Chicago. The Canadiens won the game 5–4 and swept the Blackhawks to claim the Cup. Who was the goalie who made the big stop?

12) The record for most points in one period of a playoff game is four. The first player to hit the mark, with three goals and an assist, was a Canadien. He did it during a 10–3 triumph over the Toronto Maple Leafs at the Forum on March 29, 1945. Can you name him?

Centre Elmer Lach scores one of his 215 career goals for the Canadiens.

13) Montreal goaltender Bill Durnan set a modern-day record with a shutout streak that lasted 309 minutes and 21 seconds during the 1948–49 season. This mark was surpassed during the 2003–04 season, when a netminder shut out the opposition for 332:01. Who set the new mark, and what team did he play for?

14) The 1952–53 Montreal Canadiens were an interesting team that finished in second place but knocked off Chicago and Boston to win the Stanley Cup. The team set a club record (for a minimum 70-game schedule) that would not be normally

associated with the "Flying Frenchmen." What team mark was set?

15) This Montreal player tied an NHL record (first set by Maurice Richard) when he registered eight points (four goals and four assists) in a game on January 9, 1954, in which the Canadiens whipped the Chicago Blackhawks 12–1. Who was he?

16) This Montreal Canadien was the first NHL player to record six points (two goals and four assists) in one playoff game when the Habs walloped the Boston Bruins 8–1 on March 25, 1954. The record was equalled many times over the years, but was not surpassed until

Wayne Gretzky had a seven-point playoff game in 1985 (the record is now eight, held jointly by Patrik Sundstrom and Mario Lemieux). Who was the high-scoring Hab?

17) True or false: the Montreal Canadiens share the NHL record (based on a minimum 70-game schedule) for allowing the fewest goals in one season.

18) He was the first Montreal Canadien to win the Art Ross Trophy (awarded to the player credited with the most points during the regular season) two years in a row. During one of those years, he won the scoring title despite playing with a broken wrist for most

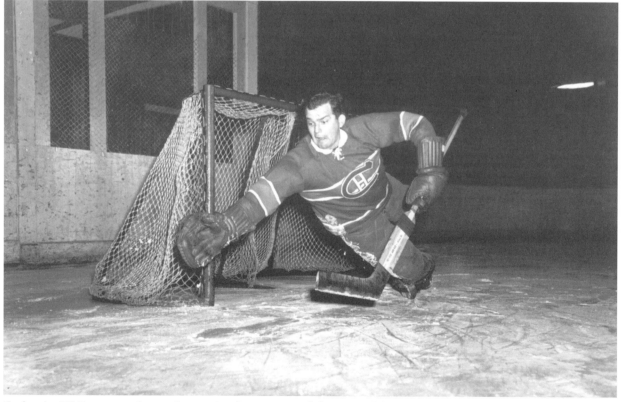

Goaltender Bill Durnan was known for wearing the same type of glove on each hand.

Claude Provost (#14) was nicknamed "Joe."

times in seven years. (He won it once more, as a New York Ranger.) It was a teammate who took the award in 1959, denying Harvey a run of seven in a row. Can you name that teammate and fellow Hall of Fame defenceman?

21) The Montreal Canadiens were so dominant in the late '50s that they held a near monopoly on the All-Star teams named at the end of the season. For example, after the 1958–59 season, six of the 12 All-Stars were Canadiens. Can you name all six?

22) This Montreal centre was named the rookie of the year for the 1958–59 season when he beat out Toronto defenceman Carl Brewer for the Calder Trophy. He scored 18 goals in his first year and would go on to score 215 goals and 502 points in 844 games as a Canadien. Who was he?

of the season! Who was this tough and determined Hab?

19) The NHL record for the fastest goal from the start of a period is four seconds, and it was set by a Canadiens right winger on the night of November 9, 1957, in a 4–2 win over Boston. Who set the record, and who tied it in 1986? *Hint: The player who tied the record was a Chicago Blackhawk who would go on to play for the Canadiens.*

20) As a Canadien, Doug Harvey won the Norris Trophy as the NHL's best defenceman a total of six

Doug Harvey (#2) was a great all-round athlete who excelled at hockey.

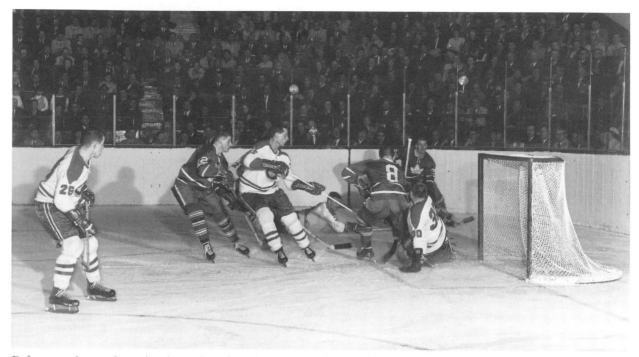

Defenceman Jacques Laperriere (centre) was born in Rouyn, Quebec, and had a Hall of Fame career with the Canadiens.

23) From October 18, 1959, to November 29, 1959, one of the great Montreal teams of all time went 15–0–3 during an 18-game stretch. What did they do in each and every game during that streak?

24) On December 12, 1963, the Montreal Canadiens and New York Rangers set an NHL record by combining to score three goals in just 18 seconds in the first period of a game won by the Habs 6–4. (The mark was shattered 20 years later when Minnesota and the Rangers scored three times in 15 seconds.) Camille Henry of the Rangers scored one of the goals, while the other two markers came from the Canadiens. Who were the two Hab goal scorers?

25) True or false: the NHL record for most ties in one season is 23, set by the Montreal Canadiens in 1962–63.

26) The NHL playoff record for most assists in one period of a game is three, and it has been accomplished many times. One Montreal player who tied the mark did so during the seventh game of the 1965 Stanley Cup finals between the Canadiens and Blackhawks. This right winger was in on three goals scored during the first period of the game, which Montreal won 4–0. Who was the player? *Hint: He was the NHL's rookie of the year in 1962.*

27) The Montreal Canadiens played in one of their wildest playoff games ever on April 14, 1966. In the first period, they set an NHL

record with 66 minutes in penalties, drawing six majors, three minors and three 10-minute misconducts. (The current record, set by the New York Rangers in 1981, is 125.) Who did the Habs play and beat that evening by a 4–1 score?

28) Can you name the only Montreal defence-man to win both the Calder Trophy (as rookie of the year) and the Norris Trophy (the NHL's best defenceman)?

29) On December 7, 1967, during a game at the Forum between Montreal and Detroit, this Canadien was assessed what was believed to be the first-ever triple minor on one play. At 11:57 of the first period, he was penalized two minutes each for charging, high-sticking and slashing after a confrontation with Gary Bergman of the Red Wings. Can you name him?

30) The first player to win the Conn Smythe Trophy (given to the best player in the play-offs) and the first defenceman to win the coveted award were both members of the Montreal Canadiens. Can you name them?

31) How many games long is the Canadiens' team record for most consecutive wins? Is it 12, 15 or 18?

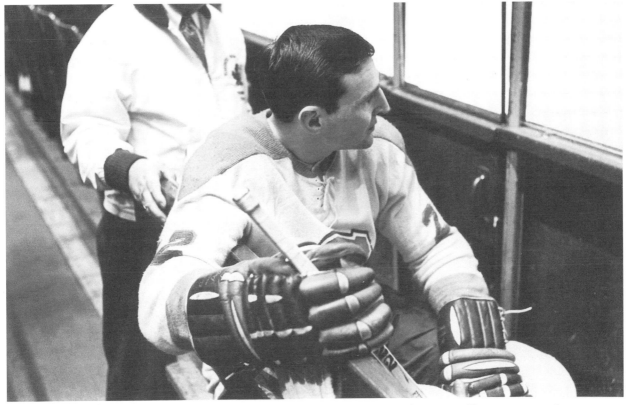

John Ferguson (#22) was one of the most rugged and feared players when he played for Montreal between 1963 and 1971.

Serge Savard was part of eight Stanley Cup teams with the Canadiens.

February 20, 1971, at the Forum. Which Hab accomplished this fast feat?

34) Goaltender Ken Dryden was first called up to the Montreal Canadiens late in the 1970–71 season, and after he posted a perfect 6–0 record he earned the starting assignment in the playoffs. He took the Habs past Boston, Minnesota and Chicago and earned his first major individual award when he won the Conn Smythe Trophy. Which other major award did he win the following year, in 1971–72?

32) The Bill Masterton Trophy has been awarded annually since 1968 to the NHL player who best exemplifies the qualities of perseverance, sportsmanship and dedication to hockey. Four Montreal Canadiens have been honoured with this trophy, including the first-ever recipient. Who was the first winner of the trophy, and who are the other three winners from Montreal?

33) Helping his team to a 7–1 win against the Chicago Blackhawks, this Montreal centre scored two goals in five seconds (just one second short of the NHL record) on

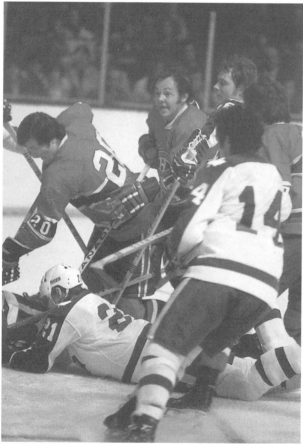

Montreal's Peter Mahovlich (#20) crashes the Toronto net looking for a goal.

35) Which player set a Canadiens playoff record with 27 points (14 goals, 13 assists) during the 1971 playoffs?

36) Which Montreal player set a modern-day team record with 15 goals in one playoff year during the 1973 post-season?

37) Held by three different players, the NHL record for the fastest goal from the start of a game is five seconds. But for more than eight years the record was six seconds, and that

Guy Lapointe had a great shot from the point on the power-play and scored 166 career goals for Montreal.

mark was set in a game between the Canadiens and the Detroit Red Wings on January 28, 1973. Which Red Wing scored the goal to help his team win the game 4–2?

38) This centre played in a club-record 560 consecutive games for the Montreal Canadiens (from October 8, 1975, through April 4, 1982). His iron-man streak continued through stints with Washington and Hartford, and he retired having played in an NHL-record 964 consecutive games. Who is he?

Frank Mahovlich (#27) was acquired by Montreal in a deal with Detroit in 1971.

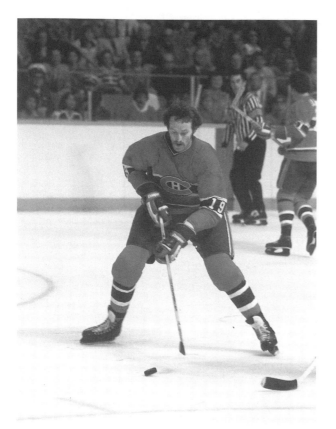

Larry Robinson was a three time first team all-star during his career with Montreal.

wins, 8 losses and 12 ties). Needless to say, they won the Cup. The Detroit Red Wings of 1995–96 are second, with 131 points (they racked up 62 wins, 13 losses and 7 ties, but did not win the Stanley Cup). Which team holds the third-best mark?

41) Wingers Steve Shutt and Guy Lafleur share one very significant team record for scoring. Can you name the standard these two Hall of Fame players have both set?

42) The 1974–75 Montreal Canadiens set an NHL record for playing in the most road games without a loss. How many games long was the streak: 15, 20, 23 or 25?

43) The Montreal Canadiens were the first team to have two defencemen score 20 or more goals in a season. It happened during the 1974–75 campaign. Can you name the pair of defenders?

39) Only one Montreal Canadien has ever won the Lester B. Pearson Award (given to the most valuable player in the NHL as voted by the players), and he did it three years in a row. Who is the player?

40) The 1976–77 Montreal Canadiens hold the NHL record for most points in one season with 132 (based on a record of 60

Mats Naslund (#26) came to the Canadiens from his native Sweden.

Scotty Bowman coached the Canadiens to five Stanley Cups (1973, 1976, 1977, 1978 and 1979).

44) During the 1972–73 season, this Montreal winger scored 18 goals on 68 shots for a league-best 26.5% shooting percentage. Who was the Montreal sharpshooter?
Hint: The player was in his rookie season.

45) Which Montreal defenceman led the entire NHL in plus/minus with a rating of plus-78 in 1972–73?
Hint: He's a member of the Hall of Fame.

46) The NHL record for the most 20-goal scorers on one team is 11, set by the Boston Bruins in 1977–78. Three teams trail them with 10: the 1970–71 Bruins, the 1980–81 St. Louis Blues and the 1974–75 Montreal Canadiens. Can

you name at least five of the 10 Habs who scored 20 or more goals in '74–75?

47) In 1975–76 the Montreal Canadiens recorded a league-best 127 points (on the strength of a 58–11–11 record). One of their divisional rivals finished with a grand total of 32 points (11–59–10), the worst mark of any NHL team that year. The 95-point difference between the two teams represents a league record for the greatest discrepancy from first to worst. Can you name the awful team that finished last overall?

48) This goaltender was named the best in the American Hockey League for the 1972–73

season. He went on to play with the Montreal Canadiens between 1973 and 1981, usually as the backup goalie. He posted a 16–1–3 record during the 1975–76 season and shared in a Vezina Trophy win four times with Montreal. Who was he?

49) From 1953 until 1979, the Montreal Canadiens did not lose a single regular-season home opener, winning 24 and tying three. The string was finally broken on October 11, 1980, when they dropped their home opener 5–4. Which team broke the streak?

Mark Recchi was acquired by the Canadiens in a deal with the Philadelphia Flyers.

Patrick Roy was a star goaltender for the Canadiens from 1984 to 1996.

50) Montreal left winger Bob Gainey won the Frank J. Selke Trophy as the NHL's best defensive forward for the first four years the trophy was awarded (1978–1981). He was the runner-up in 1982, when the award went to a Boston Bruins centre who was nowhere near as good as Gainey. Who was the Boston player who won the Selke in 1982?

51) The Vezina Trophy has been awarded since 1927 (under two different sets of criteria), and on only one occasion have three goalies shared the award. The three netminders guarded the nets for the Montreal Canadiens

Jose Theodore was drafted 44th overall by the Canadiens during the 1994 Entry Draft.

during the 1980–81 season. Can you name them?

52) Other than Doug Harvey, who is the only Montreal defenceman to win the Norris Trophy more than once?

53) From 1951–52 through 1982–83, the Montreal Canadiens recorded 32 straight winning seasons. What was the Habs' record in 1983–84, when the streak was broken?

54) Only five players have ever played in 1,000 regular-season games with the Montreal Canadiens. Can you name all of them?

55) Four players have recorded 100 or more points in a season for the Habs. Can you name them all?

56) Only four players have recorded their 1,000th career point while wearing a Montreal Canadiens uniform. Can you name them?

57) Jean Beliveau, Frank Mahovlich and Guy Lafleur were all members of the Canadiens when they scored their 500th career goal. Can you name the goaltender who gave up each player's milestone marker?

58) Only two Montreal Canadiens have ever won the Lady Byng Trophy, which recognizes the combination of skill with gentlemanly play. Who are they?

59) Which two players are tied for the Habs record of 71 points by a first-year player? *Hint: Both were born in Europe.*

60) The second game of the 1986 Stanley Cup finals, played on May 18, 1986, between Montreal and Calgary, went into overtime tied at 2–2. The Canadiens needed to win the game or else they would fall behind in the series by two games. They set an NHL record for the fastest game-winning goal in overtime when they won the game after just nine seconds of extra play. Which Hab scored this important goal?

61) Frank Mahovlich (on May 16, 1971, against Chicago) and Mats Naslund (on May 1, 1984,

Forward Saku Koivu came back from serious health problems in 2001–02 to score 21 goals and 71 points in 2002–03.

63) This Montreal goaltender became the first NHL netminder to win the Vezina Trophy (best goalie) and at least a share of the Jennings Trophy (fewest goals allowed) in the same season. Can you name him?

64) The second period of the March 11, 1989, game between Montreal and Hartford produced an NHL record for the fastest three goals from the start of a period (1:05). Kevin Dineen of the Whalers scored one goal, while the other two were chipped in by members of the Canadiens. Who were they?

65) Can you name the first two Montreal Canadiens defencemen to record five assists in one game?
Hint: They achieved this feat 39 years apart.

66) Jean Beliveau (1964), Henri Richard (1967) and Peter Mahovlich (1976) were all named most valuable player in an NHL All-Star Game. Which Hab was named the player of the game during the 1997 All-Star classic?

67) Only two players have ever recorded six points in a road game. The first was Joe Malone, during the NHL's inaugural season of 1917–18. The second, a winger who scored four goals and added two assists, did it on January 8, 1998, during an 8–2 win over the New York Islanders. Who is the left winger who tied the mark?

68) The NHL record for most points in one period is held by Bryan Trottier, who had a big second period (three goals and three assists for six points) during a game between the New York Islanders and the New York Rangers. A number of players have recorded

against the New York Islanders) are the only two Montreal Canadiens to take penalty shots in the playoffs. Both players were foiled in their attempts. Which goalies stopped them?
Hint: Both goalies are in the Hall of Fame.

62) Only two Montreal Canadiens coaches have won the Jack Adams Award (presented to the coach of the year). Who are they?

five points in one period, including one Canadien who accomplished the feat on February 14, 1990, when the Habs knocked off Vancouver 10–1 at the Forum. He had two goals and three assists in the first period of the game. Who is he?

69) It shouldn't come as a surprise that the three teams who have won the most regular-season games are from the NHL's "Original Six" era. Can you name the three teams, ranking them by the number of games they've won?

70) The Canadiens have a losing playoff record against just one NHL team (of teams they have met in the playoffs more than once). They have battled this team 12 times in the playoffs, but won only five of the series while losing seven. Can you name the only team that has bested the Canadiens in the postseason?

71) Wayne Gretzky holds the all-time record with 10 playoff hat tricks; his longtime winger, Jari Kurri, is tied for second with seven postseason hat tricks. Which Montreal superstar also recorded seven hat tricks in the playoffs: Maurice Richard, Guy Lafleur or Jean Beliveau?

72) Maurice Richard is generally acknowledged as one of the best players in the history of the NHL, but he was rarely recognized as such during his playing days. How many times did he win the Hart Trophy as the league's most valuable player?

73) Two Montreal goaltenders won the Vezina Trophy and the Hart Trophy in the same season. Can you name them?

74) Three Canadiens have won the Hart Trophy on more than one occasion. Who are they, and how many times did each player win the award that honours the most valuable player in the NHL?

75) He had his name inscribed on the Stanley Cup an astounding 17 times during the course of his employment with the Montreal Canadiens, both on and off the ice. Who is he?

Forward Michael Ryder (#73) is a native of St. John's, Newfoundland.

76) The Montreal Canadiens own the NHL marks for most Stanley Cups (23) and most appearances in the finals (32), but which team holds the record for making the play-offs in the most years?

77) Since the founding of the Boston Bruins in 1924, they have met the Canadiens 30 times in the Stanley Cup playoffs. What is the Habs' record against the Bruins in those 30 meetings?

78) This player set a Montreal team record for defencemen when he recorded six points (a goal and five assists) in one game as the Canadiens beat Pittsburgh 8–0 on January 4, 2004. Can you name him?

Hall of Fame defenceman Tom Johnson (#10) is a native of Baldur, Manitoba.

79) Which Montreal rookie led all first-year players in points during the 2003–04 season?

80) True or false: on the list of teams that suffered the fewest losses in one season (based on a minimum 70-game schedule), the Montreal Canadiens hold the top four slots.

Answers

1) Newsy Lalonde
2) Odie Cleghorn (brother of Sprague)
3) Harry Cameron and Sprague Cleghorn
4) George Hainsworth
5) Hainsworth, who recorded 75 career shutouts for Montreal

Maurice Richard was a clutch playoff performer with the Canadiens scoring 82 post-season goals for the team.

6) Armand Mondou

7) Toe Blake

8) Alex Smart

9) J.C. Tremblay

10) Elmer Lach

11) Bill Durnan

12) Maurice Richard

13) Brian Boucher of the Phoenix Coyotes

14) The 1952–53 Canadiens set a team record for fewest goals scored, with 155.

15) Bert Olmstead

16) Dickie Moore

17) True. Both the Montreal Canadiens (1955–56) and the Toronto Maple Leafs (1953–54) share the mark of 131 goals against.

18) Dickie Moore

Jean Beliveau recorded 1,219 points (507 goals, 712 assists) in his career with Montreal.

19) Claude Provost set the mark, and Denis Savard tied it.

20) Tom Johnson

21) On the first team: goaltender Jacques Plante, defenceman Tom Johnson and forwards Jean Beliveau and Dickie Moore. On the second team: defenceman Doug Harvey and forward Henri Richard.

22) Ralph Backstrom

23) Montreal scored the opening goal in each contest.

24) Dave Balon and Gilles Tremblay

25) False. The Philadelphia Flyers tied 24 games in 1969–70.

26) Bobby Rousseau

27) The Toronto Maple Leafs

28) Jacques Laperriere won the Calder Trophy in 1964 and the Norris Trophy in 1966.

29) John Ferguson

30) Jean Beliveau (1965) and Serge Savard (1969)

31) The longest winning streak in Habs history lasted 12 games, from January 6, 1968, until February 3, 1968.

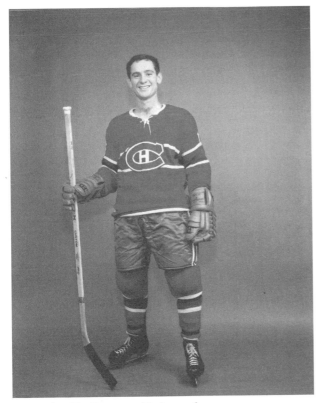

Forward Bobby Rousseau (#15) scored an even 200 career goals while with the Canadiens.

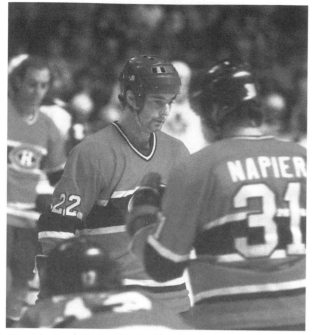

Steve Shutt was drafted by the Canadiens after a stellar junior career with the Toronto Marlies.

32) Claude Provost was the first winner of the Masterton. The others are Henri Richard (1974), Serge Savard (1979) and Saku Koivu (2002).

33) Peter Mahovlich

34) Dryden won the Calder Trophy as rookie of the year in 1972.

35) Frank Mahovlich

36) Yvan Cournoyer

37) Henry Boucha

38) Doug Jarvis

39) Guy Lafleur (1976–1978)

40) That would be the Stanley Cup–winning Montreal Canadiens of 1977–78, with 129 points.

41) Both have scored a team-record 60 goals in one season. Shutt did it in 1976–77, while Lafleur scored his 60 a year later.

42) Between November 27, 1974, and March 12, 1975, the Habs played 23 games without a defeat, going 14–0–9.

Goaltender Richard Sevigny posted a very respectable 67–41–17 record in 141 career games with Montreal.

Guy Lafleur made his debut as a Montreal Canadien during the 1971–72 season.

43) Guy Lapointe (28 goals) and Serge Savard (20)

44) Murray Wilson

45) Jacques Laperriere

46) Yvan Cournoyer (29 goals), Guy Lafleur (53), Yvon Lambert (32), Guy Lapointe (28), Jacques Lemaire (36), Peter Mahovlich (35), Serge Savard (20), Steve Shutt (30), Mario Tremblay (21) and Murray Wilson (24)

47) The Washington Capitals

48) Michel Larocque

49) The Chicago Blackhawks

50) Steve Kasper

51) Denis Herron, Michel Larocque and Richard Sevigny

52) Larry Robinson (1977 and 1980)

53) The Canadiens posted a 35–40–5 record in 1983–84.

54) Henri Richard (1,256 games), Larry Robinson (1,202), Bob Gainey (1,160), Jean Beliveau (1,125) and Claude Provost (1,005)

55) Guy Lafleur (six times), Peter Mahovlich (twice), Steve Shutt (once) and Mats Naslund (once)

56) Jean Beliveau (1968), Frank Mahovlich (1973), Henri Richard (1973) and Guy Lafleur (1981)

57) Beliveau scored on Gilles Gilbert of Minnesota on February 11, 1971; Mahovlich's victim was Dunc Wilson of Vancouver on March 21, 1973; and Lafleur scored his 500th against Glenn Resch of Colorado on December 20, 1983.

58) Toe Blake in 1946 and Mats Naslund in 1988

59) Mats Naslund (1982–83) and Kjell Dahlin (1985–86)

60) Brian Skrudland

61) Tony Esposito of Chicago and Billy Smith of New York

62) Scotty Bowman (1977) and Pat Burns (1989)

Henri Richard was made captain of the Canadiens in 1971 after the retirement of Jean Beliveau.

63) Patrick Roy

64) Petr Svoboda and Guy Carbonneau

65) Doug Harvey was first, in a 10–2 win over the
New York Rangers on March 19, 1955, followed by
Lyle Odelein, in a 9–2 win over Hartford on
February 2, 1994.

66) Mark Recchi

67) Brian Savage

68) Stephane Richer

69) As of the end of the 2003–04 season, the Montreal
Canadiens led with 2,849 all-time victories,
followed by the Boston Bruins (2,564) and Toronto
Maple Leafs (2,418).

Although forward Brian Savage was selected 171st overall in
1991, he scored 155 goals and 285 points as a Hab.

70) The Detroit Red Wings (the Canadiens are 0–1
against both Edmonton and New Jersey in the playoffs for their only other losing records).

71) Maurice Richard

72) He won the Hart Trophy once, in 1947, and was the
runner-up twice, in 1945 and 1951.

73) Jacques Plante (1962) and Jose Theodore (2002)

74) Howie Morenz (three times—1928, 1931, 1932), Jean
Beliveau (twice—1956 and 1964) and Guy Lafleur
(twice—1977 and 1978)

75) Jean Beliveau won 10 Stanley Cups as a player
and was a Canadiens executive for another seven
championships.

Defenceman Petr Svoboda scored four goals and added 27
assists as a rookie in 1984–85.

76) Including 2003–04, the Canadiens have made the playoffs a record 74 times in 87 years. The Toronto Maple Leafs are next, with 64 appearances in 87 years, while the Boston Bruins have been in the playoffs 62 times in 80 years.

77) As of 2004, the Canadiens are 23–7 versus the Bruins in the playoffs.

78) Sheldon Souray

79) Michael Ryder

80) True. Montreal lost eight games in 1976–77, 10 in 1972–73 and 1977–78 and 11 in 1975–76.

Sheldon Souray

3

Trades

1) One of the best defencemen of his era, this goal-scoring blueliner won two Stanley Cups with the Ottawa Senators before the Canadiens acquired him on November 26, 1921, in a trade with the Hamilton Tigers. The Canadiens gave up Harry Mummery and Amos Arbour to acquire this future Hall of Famer, who won a third Cup with Montreal in 1924. Can you name him?

2) A member of the Montreal Canadiens in 1917–18, their first National Hockey League season (which saw him score an amazing 44 goals in 20 games), this centre went on to play for Quebec and Hamilton before the Habs re-acquired him in a December 22, 1922, deal that sent Edmond Bouchard to the Hamilton Tigers. Can you name this high-scoring forward?

3) Newsy Lalonde's career with the Canadiens dated back to their days in the National Hockey Association. In their first five NHL seasons, Lalonde continued to star for the Habs, registering 124 goals and 165 points in 98 games. On September 18, 1922, he was traded to the Saskatoon Sheiks of the Western Canada Hockey League. Can you name the legendary player Montreal acquired in this deal?

Hint: He wore a cap during games.

Defenceman Sprague Cleghorn played on Montreal's Stanley Cup–winning team of 1924.

4) On a whim, Toronto general manager Conn Smythe offered his star goalie, Lorne Chabot, to the Canadiens—and, much to his surprise, a deal was completed on October 1, 1933. In exchange, the Leafs received a netminder who had led the league in shutouts three times in his career with Montreal. Who was sent to Toronto?

5) After many great years with the Canadiens, the legendary Howie Morenz was traded away to the Chicago Blackhawks, along with goalie Lorne Chabot and defenceman Marty Burke, on October 3, 1934. Montreal management felt a change was best for Morenz, although it did not prove to be of any benefit to the one-time star. The Habs received three players in return. Can you name them?

6) The Montreal Maroons did the Canadiens a big favour when they sent centre Hector "Toe" Blake to the Habs in a trade on February 13, 1936. It began an association between Blake and the Canadiens—as a player, coach and executive—that would last until his death. The Maroons threw a couple of other players into the deal in exchange for a goaltender. Who was the netminder the Maroons took in the swap?

7) After a long career with the Montreal Maroons, New York Rangers and Boston Bruins, this defenceman was acquired by the Canadiens in a trade completed on September 10, 1936. Montreal also received Roger Jenkins in the deal while giving up Leroy Goldsworthy and Sammy McManus. This rearguard would win the Hart Trophy for the 1936–37 season and was named coach of the Habs in 1939. Can you name him?

Left winger Aurel Joliat was small (5'7", 136 pounds) but he was a prolific goal scorer (270 goals) for the Canadiens.

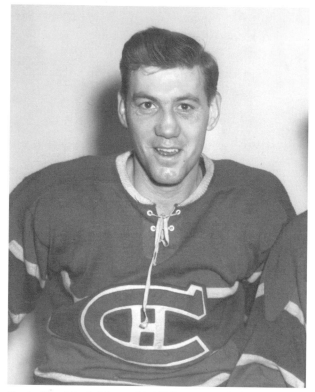

Centre Ken Mosdell began his NHL career with the Brooklyn Americans in 1941–42.

8) The Canadiens owned the playing rights to Ted Kennedy (now a member of the Hall of Fame), but when Kennedy made it clear that he did not want to play in Montreal, a deal was made to send his rights to Toronto on September 10, 1943. In exchange, the Canadiens received the rights to a defence-man they originally owned. Who was this blueliner?

9) One of the Habs' better trades took place with the Detroit Red Wings on September 11, 1945, when they acquired a small but effective centre in exchange for Ray Getliffe, Roly Rossignol and, later, the rights to Fern Gauthier. This pivot would play the rest of his career in Montreal, winning two Stanley

Cups (in 1946 and 1953) and scoring 103 goals and 265 points before retiring. He went on to become a well-known coach in Chicago. Can you name him?

10) A two-time winner of the Stanley Cup (1944 and 1946), this centre was acquired by the Habs in a cash deal with the Montreal Maroons on September 24, 1938. He was involved in an unpopular trade on August 19, 1947, when he and defenceman Frank Eddolls were sent to the New York Rangers in exchange for three players. Perhaps adding insult to injury, this player was named the NHL's most valuable player for the 1947–48 season. Can you name him?

11) Veteran right winger Joe Carveth came to the Habs in a December 1947 trade with Boston and scored one goal in 35 games. He had a good year with Montreal in 1948–49, scoring 15 goals in 60 games, but the Canadiens decided to move him back to Detroit. On November 11, 1949, Carveth, who had won the Stanley Cup with the Red Wings in 1943, was dealt to Detroit where he won another cup in 1950. In return, the Canadiens received a left winger who helped them win a Cup in 1953, even though he only appeared in the playoffs (four points in seven games) that season. What was his name?

12) Right winger Leo Gravelle had a couple of good seasons with the Canadiens (16 goals in 1946–47 and 19 in 1949–50), but Montreal made a very good trade in sending him to the Detroit Red Wings on December 19, 1950. The Habs received a hard-nosed left winger who helped the Canadiens win four

Stanley Cups. Can you name him?
Hint: He also won a Stanley Cup with Toronto in 1962.

13) This centre broke into the NHL with the Brooklyn Americans, and when that team folded the Canadiens chose him in a special dispersal draft. The war delayed his Montreal debut until 1944–45; he went on to win three Stanley Cups with the Habs (in 1946, 1953 and 1956) and put together back-to-back 22-goal seasons before he was sent to Chicago along with Bud MacPherson on May 17, 1956. The Canadiens held the right of recall on this player and re-acquired him in September of 1957. He spent most of the next two seasons in the minors, but won another Cup in 1959, when he was called up for the playoffs. Who

Dave Balon (#20) won two Stanley Cups (1965 and 1966) with the Canadiens.

was this Canadiens player, and what did Montreal receive in return for the two players when they made the trade in '56?

14) This big (6'3", 192 pounds) left winger first joined the Canadiens in 1957–58 and promptly won three straight Stanley Cups. He was seen as a potential star, but a nine-goal season in 1959–60 seemed to changed the minds of Montreal management. A trade was made with Chicago on June 7, 1960. The Habs also gave up Reggie Fleming, Bob Courcy and Cec Hoekstra. Who was the main player the Habs dealt to the Blackhawks, and who did the Canadiens get back?

15) Despite his All-Star status and his numerous Norris Trophies, the Canadiens wanted to move team captain Doug Harvey off the team (reportedly for his involvement in organizing the ill-starred NHL Players Association of the late '50s). He was dealt to the New York Rangers on June 13, 1961, and he won another Norris Trophy as the NHL's best defenceman in 1961–62. In return for the outstanding veteran, the Canadiens received a tough blueliner without anywhere near the talent of Harvey. Can you name him?
Hint: "Leapin Louie" is best remembered for a fight he lost against Gordie Howe in 1958.

16) Coach Toe Blake was so fed up with the quirky antics of goalie Jacques Plante by the end of the 1962–63 season that he made it clear to general manager Frank Selke that the six-time Vezina Trophy winner had to be dealt. A trade was consummated on June 4, 1963, in which Plante and two other Habs headed to the Big Apple, while four New

Winger Dick Duff was known to play his best hockey in the playoffs.

York Rangers came to Montreal. Can you name all of the other players involved in one of hockey's biggest trades?

17) It was an unheralded trade at the time, but in June of 1964 the Canadiens sent two players (Guy Allen and Paul Reid) they had selected in that year's Amateur Draft to Boston for two players the Bruins had taken in the same draft. One of the players obtained in the deal turned out to be a six-time Stanley Cup winner and a Hall of Fame member. Who was he?

18) Prior to the start of the 1963–64 season, the Canadiens were looking to add a rugged

blueliner to their squad. They found their man with the Springfield Indians of the American Hockey League, and in June 1963 they pulled off an 11-player swap of mostly minor leaguers to get him. It was a wise investment; this rearguard provided muscle and helped Montreal to four Stanley Cups. Can you name him?
Hint: He also won a Stanley Cup with Philadelphia in 1975.

19) When this player was with Toronto he was known as a clutch playoff performer—he won two Stanley Cups with the Maple Leafs. He was dealt to New York but could not adjust to playing for the Rangers, so the Habs decided to give him a chance. They sent Bill Hicke to Broadway in a trade completed on December 22, 1964. Who was the player the Canadiens acquired?
Hint: This player would win four Cups with Montreal.

20) On June 10, 1968, general manager Sam Pollock made one of his patent moves when he dealt veteran Claude Larose and youngster Danny Grant to the expansion Minnesota North Stars in return for their first-round draft choice in 1972. What player did the Habs select with that pick?

21) Bryan Watson was a journeyman defence-man (and sometimes a pesky right winger) who played most of his NHL career in Detroit, Pittsburgh and Washington. He was twice the property of the Canadiens, and was traded away both times. The second of the two transactions, completed on June 28, 1968, landed the Canadiens a first-round pick in the 1972

Amateur Draft from the Oakland Seals. Which goaltender did the Habs select with this draft choice?

22) One of the best trades the Habs completed was the acquisition of centre Peter Mahovlich from the Detroit Red Wings on June 6, 1969. Mahovlich won four Stanley Cups with the Canadiens and had five seasons of 30 or more goals. Which two players did the Habs send to Detroit in exchange for Mahovlich?

23) Perhaps the greatest trade in the history of the Montreal Canadiens was made on May 22, 1970, when Sam Pollock acquired the

Oakland Seals' first-round draft choice in 1971. At the time, it wasn't a certainty that this would turn out to be the first pick overall, but the move paid off for the Habs, who went on to select Guy Lafleur. What did the Canadiens give the Seals in this trade?

24) After the Canadiens missed the 1970 playoffs, changes were made to create roster spots for some younger players. One veteran traded away on June 10, 1970, was Bobby Rousseau, who was dealt to the Minnesota North Stars. Ironically, the player acquired in the deal was a former Hab veteran. Can you name him?

Defenceman Ted Harris (left) keeps Toronto's Peter Stemkowski away from the Canadiens net. Noel Price (#23) is the other Montreal blueliner in the photo.

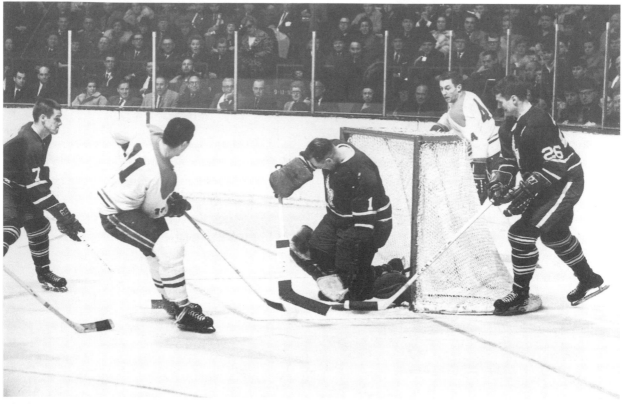

Claude Larose (#11) tries to score on Toronto netminder Johnny Bower.

25) The January 13, 1971, addition of Frank Mahovlich proved to be a crucial one. With help from "The Big M," the Habs not only returned to the playoffs, but also won the Stanley Cup that spring. Which three players did Montreal send to Detroit to complete the trade?

26) When it appeared as though the Los Angeles Kings might finish last in the NHL's West Division in 1970–71, the Canadiens had cause for concern. They owned the Oakland Seals' first-round pick in the upcoming Amateur Draft and were counting on the Seals to occupy the basement. Habs general manager Sam Pollock did his best to make sure that the Kings finished ahead of Oakland; on January 26, 1971, he shipped an unhappy centre to the Kings in exchange for Ray Fortin and Gord Labossiere. Who was the Montreal player in the deal?

27) After Ken Dryden's remarkable performance in the 1971 playoffs, goaltender Rogie Vachon realized he no longer fit into the Canadiens' future plans. He asked for, and was granted, a trade to the Los Angeles Kings on November 4, 1971. The Kings gave up four players in return for the three-time Stanley Cup winner. Can you name them?

28) Right winger Phil Roberto had a pretty good year for a rookie in 1970–71, scoring 14 goals and totalling 21 points in just 39 games. He then appeared in 15 playoff games and got his name on the Stanley Cup for the only time in his career. But when Scotty Bowman took over as coach of the Habs, he jumped at the chance to re-acquire a veteran. On December 13, 1971, Roberto was sent to the Blues in exchange for a right winger/defenceman who had started his career with Montreal. Who was he?

29) Veteran defenceman Terry Harper, a five-time Stanley Cup winner (1965, 1966, 1968, 1969 and 1971), did not enjoy playing for coach Scotty Bowman, so he asked for a trade. He was granted his wish on August 22, 1972, when he was dealt to the Los Angeles Kings. How many draft choices did the Canadiens receive in return?

30) By the end of the 1972–73 season, the Canadiens really did not have room to keep defenceman Bob Murdoch on the team, even though he had contributed to two Stanley Cups (1971 and 1973). The Los Angeles Kings were interested, and the Habs added Randy Rota to the deal completed on May 29, 1973. In keeping with what seemed to be standard practice for the Kings, they gave away their first-round draft choice in 1974 in the deal. Which player did the Habs select with the pick?

31) When the Canadiens realized that first-round draft choice Dave Gardner was not going to work out as anticipated (after 36 games with the team), they moved quickly to acquire something of value in return for him.

The St. Louis Blues felt the former junior star still had potential, and on March 9, 1974, they gave up a first-round draft choice to secure him. Which player did the Canadiens select with this pick?

32) Left winger Chuck Lefley enjoyed a couple of good seasons (21 and 23 goals) as a member of the Canadiens in the early '70s. He was also on two Cup-winning teams (1971 and 1973) with the Habs, but he was dealt to the St. Louis Blues on November 28, 1974. Who did the Canadiens receive in return?

The feisty Doug Riseborough (#8) recorded 959 penalty minutes in 493 games as a Hab.

33) When goaltender Ken Dryden sat out the entire 1973–74 season in search of a better contract, Wayne Thomas did an admirable job as part of the group that replaced him, posting a 23–12–5 record. Dryden's return forced Thomas to the sidelines—he did not play a single minute in 1974–75. In spite of that fact, the Toronto Maple Leafs felt he had value, and on June 17, 1975, they traded their first-round pick in the 1976 draft to acquire him. What player did the Canadiens take with the selection?

34) Sam Pollock pulled off one of the great steals of all time when he sent minor-league forward Greg Hubick to the Toronto Maple Leafs on June 26, 1975. The player the Canadiens received had not yet played a single game in the NHL, but he went on to win four straight Stanley Cups after putting on a Habs uniform. Can you name him? *Hint: He was a very durable player.*

35) By 1977–78, Peter Mahovlich had worn out his welcome in Montreal. The Canadiens packaged him with a former first-round pick and made a deal with the Pittsburgh Penguins on November 29, 1977. Who was the former draft choice the Habs added to the deal, and which player did the Canadiens receive from Pittsburgh?

36) Left winger Murray Wilson won three Stanley Cups with the Canadiens (in 1973, 1976 and 1977) and enjoyed his best season in 1974–75, when he had a career-high 24 goals and 42 points. On October 5, 1978, he was dealt to the Los Angeles Kings, along with a first-round draft choice (in 1979), in return for a first-round choice in 1981. Name the

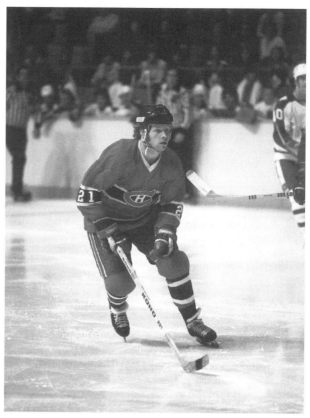

Centre Doug Jarvis (#21) scored 91 goals and 154 assists during his career with the Canadiens.

player the Kings selected with their pick, and the player the Habs took with theirs.

37) Although he was picked 13th overall by Montreal in 1976, this left winger played in only two games for the Canadiens before he was dealt to the Pittsburgh Penguins on October 18, 1978, in exchange for a first-round draft choice in the 1981 entry draft. Who was the player Montreal traded, and who was the player they selected with the draft pick?

38) Born in Caracas, Venezuela, defenceman/ right winger Rick Chartraw won four Stanley

Defenceman Robert Picard (right) played parts of four seasons with the Canadiens before he was sent to Winnipeg.

Cups (1976–79) in Montreal and played on another Cup winner in Edmonton (1984) during his NHL career. He was essentially a role player who could play it tough when necessary. Like many other role players on the great Montreal teams, he was dealt to the Los Angeles Kings on February 17, 1981, in exchange for a second-round draft choice. Who did the Habs take with the choice?
Hint: The player chosen made a key contribution to the Canadiens' Stanley Cup win in 1986.

39) The only member of the 1980 gold-medal-winning U.S. Olympic Team to be selected by the Montreal Canadiens was a defence-man picked 54th overall in the 1976 Amateur Draft. This blueliner played all of 11 games for the Habs in 1980–81 before being dealt to the Colorado Rockies that same season. The Habs were able to get a third-round draft choice for the rearguard, whose NHL career lasted 143 games. Can you name him?

40) Michel "Bunny" Larocque was a very good backup netminder to Ken Dryden during the Habs dynasty of the '70s. When other goalies were brought in to play after Dryden's retirement, Larocque was moved in a deal with the Toronto Maple Leafs on March 10, 1981. In return, the Leafs sent Montreal a blueliner who had once been selected third overall by the Washington Capitals in the 1977 Amateur Draft. By 1983–84 the Canadiens had dealt him to the Winnipeg Jets. Can you name him?

41) All-Star defenceman Guy Lapointe, a six-time Stanley Cup winner with the Habs, was moved to the St. Louis Blues on March 9, 1982, as his career neared its end. The deal saw the Canadiens acquire a second-round draft choice in 1983 that they used very wisely. Who did the Habs select with their choice?
Hint: The player selected was a member of the Canadiens' Stanley Cup team in 1986.

42) One of the most controversial trades in Canadiens history took place on September 9, 1982, when they sent defenceman Rod Langway to the Washington Capitals along with rearguard Brian Engblom and forwards Doug Jarvis and Craig Laughlin. Montreal management really had no choice: Langway had insisted he wanted to play in the United

States for tax reasons. Langway went on to win the Norris Trophy and eventually gained entry into the Hockey Hall of Fame. What two players did the Canadiens receive in return?

43) In two separate transactions, the Canadiens sent centre Dan Daoust and defenceman Gaston Gingras to Toronto on December 17, 1982. Both players had been considered good prospects at one point, but management decided to give others a more prominent role on the team. The Habs received a draft choice for Daoust, which they moved in another deal, but they also received a second-

round draft pick in 1986 for Gingras. That selection proved to be valuable: the left winger they chose made a strong contribution to the Habs' Stanley Cup win in 1993, racking up 10 points in 20 games. Can you name him?

44) One of the best moves that Serge Savard made as general manager was the acquisition of Bobby Smith from the Minnesota North Stars on October 28, 1983. Savard had long admired Smith's skills and felt his team needed a big centre. It took a substantial package to pry Smith loose, even though he had fallen out of favour

Benoit Brunet (#17), trying to score here against Toronto, contributed 10 points in 20 playoff games when the Canadiens won the Stanley Cup in 1993.

Montreal centre Keith Acton (#12) is about to score on former Habs goalie Michel Larocque during a game against the Maple Leafs.

with the North Stars. What did Montreal have to give up?

45) Despite scoring 25 goals in 78 games for the Canadiens in 1982–83, his third season with the team, it was obvious that Doug Wickenheiser was not going to be the star he was once touted as (Montreal, with the first-overall pick in the draft, had selected him ahead of Denis Savard in 1980). When he started 1983–84 with only five goals in 27 games, the Habs found a trading partner in the St. Louis Blues. A deal was struck on December 21, 1983. Montreal sent two additional players to the Blues and got one player back: a former first-round draft choice who

had been taken second overall in 1979. Which players did the Habs add to sweeten the deal, and who did they get back?

46) After a little more than two years as a Hab, Montreal native Robert Picard was dealt to the Winnipeg Jets on November 4, 1983. The defenceman had once been highly touted, but at this stage in his career he was seen as no more than a journeyman. Still, the Canadiens were able to secure a third-round choice in the 1984 entry draft, with which they drafted a very significant player. Who was he?

Forward Lucien DeBlois scored 26 goals and added 28 assists in 112 games as a Hab.

nine more in the playoffs) before he was sent packing to Winnipeg on June 13, 1984. In exchange the Canadiens received a native of Joliette, Quebec, who'd been the first-round draft choice of the New York Rangers in 1977. He was with the Habs when they won the Cup in 1986. Can you name him?

49) Former first-round draft choice (in 1981) Mark Hunter had a 21-goal season in 1984–85, but the Habs dealt him to St. Louis on June 15, 1985, along with defenceman Michael Dark and four draft choices. In return the Canadiens received five draft choices, all in the 1985 entry draft, one of which was a first-round pick. The Habs selected a right winger 12th overall with that choice, but he only played in 25 games for the Canadiens before he was gone. Can you name him?

50) A November 7, 1988, deal saw the Canadiens steal another good player from the Toronto Maple Leafs without giving up much in return. The player the Habs received was a former first-round pick of the Leafs (seventh overall in 1983), and he scored 22 goals in his first 64 games for Montreal during the 1988–89 season. He then had seasons of 27 and 26 goals, while the player the Leafs got in the deal scored a total of 10 goals during his brief stay in Toronto. Name the two players involved in this trade.

51) By the summer of 1990, the Canadiens felt they had no choice but to move Norris Trophy–winning defenceman Chris Chelios to another team. The Chicago Blackhawks were more than willing to take the tough, high-scoring defender from the Habs. A deal

47) June 9, 1984, saw the Canadiens make a wise move when they sent goaltender Rick Wamsley and three draft choices to the St. Louis Blues in exchange for a first- and a second-round draft choice in the 1984 entry draft. The Canadiens made the most of the two choices, taking players who would make solid contributions over many years. Can you name the two players?

48) Before Montreal acquired Perry Turnbull from St. Louis, he had strung together three consecutive seasons in which he scored 30 or more goals. However, his stay in Montreal lasted only 40 regular-season games (and

was made on June 29, 1990, and it turned out to be one of the most lopsided trades in Habs history. Which player did Chicago send to Montreal?

52) The 1989 playoffs showed clearly that winger Claude Lemieux was not on good terms with head coach Pat Burns, who told the team trainer to remain on the bench during a game in the Stanley Cup finals against Calgary when he thought Lemieux was feigning an injury. The New Jersey Devils were interested in the pesky Lemieux, and they completed a deal with Montreal on September 4, 1990, sending a right winger in return. Who was he?
Hint: This player was a first-round draft choice (second overall) of the Hartford Whalers in 1983.

53) After eight solid seasons on the Canadiens blue line (including a Stanley Cup win in 1986), defenceman Craig Ludwig was dealt to the New York Islanders on September 4, 1990. Ludwig was a stay-at-home blueliner who was especially renowned for his wide shin pads that helped him block many shots. In exchange, the Habs received another defender who quickly fell out of favour with coach Pat Burns (he lasted 32 games in Montreal). Who was the defenceman the Canadiens received in the deal?

54) The Canadiens had high hopes when they selected centre Andrew Cassels 17th overall in 1987, but they were ultimately disappointed with his performance (eight goals and 27 points in 60 games played). On September 17, 1991, they moved Cassels to the Hartford Whalers and were only able to secure a 1992

second-round draft choice in return. Name the player the Habs took with the choice.
Hint: The player chosen had a 22-goal season with Montreal in 1995–96, but would have the best years of his career in Calgary.

55) General manager Serge Savard completed one of his best deals on September 20, 1991, when he made a swap with the New Jersey Devils. In order to make the trade, Savard had to give up high-scoring Stephane Richer as well as grinding forward Tom Chorske. In return, Savard landed a top centre and a backup goaltender. Can you name the two players the Habs got in the deal?

56) Petr Svoboda was a much-ballyhooed draft selection when he was taken fifth overall by the Canadiens in the 1984 entry draft. The slightly built defenceman was on the Habs'

Centre Denis Savard (#18) had his best years in Chicago but did score 28 goals in two straight seasons.

Stanley Cup–winning team in 1986 (although he played in only eight playoff games before he was sent home), but he was ultimately an average blueliner who was often injured. The Canadiens dealt him to Buffalo on March 10, 1992. The Sabres sent a defenceman back to Montreal in the deal. Can you name him? *Hint: He was with the Canadiens when they won the Cup in 1993.*

57) Serge Savard made another major addition to his team when he obtained Vincent Damphousse in a trade with the Edmonton Oilers on August 27, 1992. It was a costly acquisition, but one that proved worthwhile, since Damphousse led the Canadiens in regular-season points in 1992–93 with 97. (It was the third different team that the slick centre/left winger had led in points in three years, Toronto and Edmonton being the others.) He then added 20 more points in the playoffs. Which three players did the Canadiens send to the Oilers to complete the transaction?

58) Brian Bellows was a Minnesota North Star for 10 seasons before the Montreal Canadiens acquired the feisty winger on August 31, 1992. The second pick overall in the 1982 entry draft had scored 30 goals for the North Stars in 1991–92 but was moved to Montreal in exchange for a speedy Habs forward who had scored only seven goals in 27 games in '91–92. Which player did the Canadiens send to the North Stars?

59) When the Canadiens sent a large (6'2", 205 pounds) defenceman to Toronto for a second-round pick on August 20, 1992,

barely anyone paid attention. Although this blueliner had played three seasons for the Habs by the time of the deal, he was far from being viewed as a vital cog in the Montreal machine. But he became a steady and dependable rearguard in Toronto who helped the resurging Maple Leafs get to the conference finals in 1993 and 1994. He would later play on a Stanley Cup–winning team with Colorado in 1996. Can you name him?

60) A former 50-goal scorer with Toronto in 1988–89, this right winger was acquired by the Canadiens on January 28, 1993. He had 18 points in 20 regular-season games with Montreal and got his name on the Stanley Cup by appearing in 11 playoff games

Left winger Ryan Walter was one of the grittier NHL forwards when he played in the league.

Centre Brian Skrudland won two Stanley Cups during his NHL career—one with Montreal (1986) and one with Dallas (1999).

(notching an assist in the last game of the finals against Los Angeles). He also played in 31 games for Montreal the next season, but was gone by the 1994–95 season. Can you name him, as well as the player the Habs gave up to get him from Calgary?

61) Guy Carbonneau started his career as a Montreal Canadien in 1980–81, when he played his first two games for the Habs. He stayed in Montreal long enough to win two Stanley Cups (1986 and 1993) and provide many years of distinguished service (221 goals and 547 points in 912 games). However, the team seemed to think the classy centre had nothing left and traded him away on August 19, 1994, getting virtually nothing in return. (Carbonneau would prove them wrong by playing on

another Cup winner with Dallas in 1999.) What did the St. Louis Blues give the Canadiens for their captain?

62) It was one of the worst trades in the history of the club. On February 9, 1995, the Canadiens were floundering and, seeking to inject some much-needed scoring into the lineup, they picked up a pretty good winger in Mark Recchi in exchange for three players. Recchi did well, recording 43 points in 39 games to finish the '94–95 season and then producing more than 70 points each of his three full seasons with Montreal. However, the Habs were forced to give up a lot to acquire the gutsy Recchi, and the loss of those players—especially one defenceman— would prove to be difficult to overcome. Which three players did Montreal send to the Flyers to complete the deal?

63) On April 5, 1995, the Canadiens swung a deal with the New York Islanders that netted slick centre Pierre Turgeon and talented defenceman Vladimir Malakhov. It was thought that Turgeon, a native of Rouyn, Quebec, would thrive in his home province, but such did not prove to be the case. The enigmatic Malakhov, meanwhile, continued to mystify the Montreal faithful. Which three players did the Habs sent to New York to complete the deal?

64) A native of Boucherville, Quebec, this defenceman was first acquired by the Canadiens on July 8, 1995, in a deal with the Winnipeg Jets that cost the Habs a second-round draft choice. The big blueliner (a one-time first-round selection, taken 14th overall by Boston in 1987) was then lost as a free

agent to the New York Rangers, but was re-acquired two years later in a deal with Chicago. At the end of the 2003–04 season the Canadiens told him he was no longer in their plans and sent him to Los Angeles. Can you name this well-travelled defenceman?

65) Early in his stint as general manager of the Canadiens, Rejean Houle was put into an impossible situation when he was forced to unload goaltender Patrick Roy. Wanting to get a trade done quickly, Houle settled on a package of players from the Colorado Avalanche on December 6, 1995. Roy and Mike Keane ended their seasons with a Stanley Cup in Colorado, while the Habs were knocked out in the first round of the playoffs by the New York Rangers. Which three players did the Canadiens get back in the deal?

66) Lyle Odelein was originally selected 141st overall by Montreal in 1986, and he was a major contributor to the team that won the Stanley Cup in 1993. But after 420 games as a Hab, in which he accumulated 1,367 penalty minutes, the tough blueliner was sent to New Jersey to complete a one-for-one trade on August 22, 1996. Montreal re-acquired a former Hab in the deal. Can you name him?

67) When Pierre Turgeon came to realize that playing in Montreal really did not suit him (he was ridiculed for his performance in the 1996 post-season), he asked for a trade. His request was granted on October 19, 1996, when he was sent to the St. Louis Blues along with Rory Fitzpatrick and Craig Conroy for two players and a fifth-round draft choice.

Can you name the two players the Habs received?

68) The Canadiens signed enforcer Donald Brashear as a free agent in 1992 after the left winger completed his junior career with Longueuil and Verdun of the Quebec Major Junior Hockey League. Brashear was easily one of the worst players in the NHL during his stay in Montreal (scoring only three goals in 111 games played), and after a verbal spat in practice with coach Mario Tremblay he

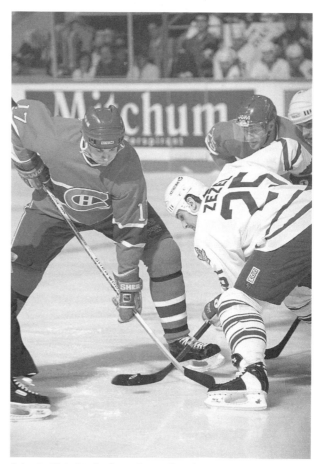

John LeClair (#17) takes a face-off against Peter Zezel of Toronto. LeClair was born in St. Albans, Vermont, and had 118 points in 224 career games with Montreal.

Stephane Richer's (#44) good shot allowed him to score 225 goals in 490 career goals as a Hab.

was dealt to Vancouver on November 13, 1996. The Habs received a defenceman in return, but they lost him on waivers early in 1997–98. Can you name him?
Hint: This defenceman played on Tampa Bay's Stanley Cup–winning team of 2004.

69) Defenceman Dave Manson was a highly sought-after player early in his career because he was tough and could score some points as well. However, by the time the Canadiens acquired the rugged blueliner his best days were a distant memory. The Habs sent two players to the Phoenix Coyotes on March 18, 1997, to complete the deal. Who were they?

70) Montreal drafted feisty winger Darcy Tucker 151st overall in the 1993 entry draft. The former Kamloops Blazer played in 115 games for the Habs, but only registered eight goals and 26 points before he was dealt to the Tampa Bay Lightning on January 15, 1998. Stephane Richer and David Wilkie accompanied Tucker to Florida in exchange for three players. Which three players were sent to the Habs in this deal?

71) The Habs realized that Dave Manson was not going to help their team in the long term, and they also came to the conclusion that Jocelyn Thibault lacked the necessary experience (and size) to play as a number-one

goalie. The two players were packaged along with Brad Brown and sent off to Chicago on November 16, 1998, for three players and a draft choice. Can you name the players the Habs received in exchange?

72) Considering that the team was not even in playoff contention at the time, the Canadiens gambled severely by sending their number-one draft choice (10th overall) to the New York Islanders on May 29, 1999, for a veteran forward who possessed great leadership skills but was in the twilight of his career. Which

Defenceman Stephane Quintal began his NHL career with the Boston Bruins.

player did the Habs get in this deal?
Hint: His best years had been spent as a Vancouver Canuck.

73) When the Canadiens decided they had had enough of defenceman Vladimir Malakhov, they dealt the blueliner to the New Jersey Devils on March 1, 2000. In return the Canadiens received a big defenceman who, after recovering from a serious wrist injury, put together a 15-goal, 35-point season for the Habs in 2003–04. His performance earned him a spot in the NHL All-Star Game. Can you name him?

74) Forward Richard Zednik has been a productive player since his acquisition from the Washington Capitals on March 13, 2001. He has posted seasons of 22, 31 and 26 goals and is one of the more dangerous Hab forwards. In the trade that saw Zednik become a Hab, the Canadiens gave up two players and a second-round draft choice while receiving one other player and a first-round selection. Can you name all of the players in this trade? And who did the Habs select with the first-round choice?

75) A native of Laval, Quebec, winger Donald Audette was picked up in a deal with the Dallas Stars on November 21, 2001. Audette had enjoyed his most productive years with the Buffalo Sabres (including a 31-goal season in 1991–92), but it was hoped he could still add some much-needed scoring punch to the Canadiens. A serious cut to his wrist scuttled those hopes, and he was moved in a deal to the Florida Panthers in 2004. Which player was sent to Montreal along with Audette,

and which two Habs were dispatched to Texas to complete the deal?

76) Although he was drafted 171st overall in 1991, left winger Brian Savage put together four seasons of 20 or more goals while he was a member of the Montreal Canadiens. When the Habs felt they could no longer afford his salary, they dealt Savage to the Phoenix Coyotes on January 25, 2002. What player did Montreal receive in return?

77) Right winger Niklas Sundstrom was a first-round selection of the New York Rangers in 1993 (eighth overall). He had a 24-goal season as a Ranger in 1996–97, but was traded away by 1999. The Canadiens picked up Sundstrom, who was now more of a checking forward, in a deal with the San Jose Sharks on January 23, 2003. Since joining Montreal he has scored 13 goals in 99 games played. Who did the Habs send to the Sharks to complete the deal?

78) When he swung a deal with the New York Rangers on March 2, 2004, Montreal general manager Bob Gainey wanted to send a message to his team—and to Habs fans— that the Canadiens were going to compete for the best players. In the transaction, Gainey picked up a very talented winger who had scored 291 career goals to date and had a Stanley Cup to his credit (with New York in 1994). Who did Montreal pick up in the deal, and what did they give up?

79) A March 2, 2004, deal saw the Canadiens acquire a centre who had won a Stanley Cup with the New Jersey Devils in 1995. He'd also played with Vancouver, New York Islanders,

Goaltender Jeff Hackett posted a 63–68–22 record with eight shutouts in 161 games with the Canadiens.

Calgary, Edmonton and Minnesota before the Habs picked him up from the Wild in return for a fourth-round draft choice. Can you name him?

80) With Jose Theodore firmly entrenched as the Canadiens' number-one goalie, it was not surprising that they dealt netminder Mathieu Garon to Los Angeles on June 26, 2004, despite his strong potential. The Habs added a second-round pick to the deal and received two players in return. Can you name them?

Joe Malone led the NHL with 44 goals in 1917–18.

Defenceman Albert "Babe" Seibert won the Hart Trophy with Montreal during the 1936–37 season.

Answers

1) Sprague Cleghorn
2) Joe Malone
3) Aurel Joliat, who scored 270 goals and 460 points in 655 games as a Canadien.
4) George Hainsworth
5) Leroy Goldsworthy, Lionel Conacher and Roger Jenkins
6) Lorne Chabot
7) Albert "Babe" Siebert
8) Frank Eddolls
9) Billy Reay
10) Buddy O'Connor
11) Calum MacKay
12) Bert Olmstead

13) Ken Mosdell. The Habs got $30,000 in cash for Mosdell and MacPherson.

14) The key Hab in this deal was Ab McDonald. Montreal received Terry Gray, Glen Skov, Lorne Ferguson, Bob Bailey and the rights to Danny Lewicki.

15) Lou Fontinato

16) Montreal sent Plante, Phil Goyette and Don Marshall to New York in return for Gump Worsley, Len Ronson, Dave Balon and Leon Rochefort.

17) Ken Dryden

18) Ted Harris

19) Dick Duff

20) Montreal selected centre Dave Gardner eighth overall.

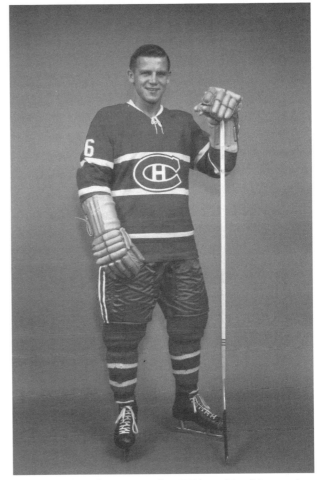

Centre Ralph Backstrom was the NHL's rookie of the year in 1958–59, when he scored 18 goals and added 22 assists.

21) Michel Larocque was selected sixth overall.

22) Garry Monahan and Doug Piper

23) Montreal sent Ernie Hicke to Oakland, along with their first pick in the 1970 Amateur Draft (the Seals took Chris Oddleifson 10th overall).

24) Claude Larose

25) Mickey Redmond, Bill Collins and Guy Charron

26) Ralph Backstrom, who produced 27 points (14 goals, 13 assists) in 33 games for the Kings to finish the '70–71 season.

27) Denis DeJordy, Dale Hoganson, Doug Robinson and Noel Price

The deal to acquire goaltender Ken Dryden (#29) was one of the best in Canadiens history.

Defenceman Rick Green (#5) played in 399 regular season games with Montreal and was on the Stanley Cup team of 1986.

28) Jimmy Roberts
29) Amazingly, the Habs got four draft choices in return for Harper: a second-round pick in 1974 (Gary MacGregor), first- and third-round selections in '75 (Pierre Mondou and Paul Woods, respectively), and a first-round choice in 1976 (Rod Schutt).
30) Mario Tremblay was picked 12th overall.
31) Doug Risebrough was selected seventh overall.
32) Don Awrey
33) Peter Lee was selected 12th overall.
34) Doug Jarvis
35) Peter Lee went with Mahovlich to Pittsburgh in exchange for Pierre Larouche.
36) The Kings selected Jay Wells, while the Habs selected Gilbert Delorme.

37) Rod Schutt was dealt to the Penguins, and the Canadiens selected Mark Hunter seventh overall with the draft choice.
38) Claude Lemieux
39) Bill Baker
40) Robert Picard
41) Sergio Momesso
42) Rick Green and Ryan Walter
43) Benoit Brunet
44) Montreal sent Mark Napier, Keith Acton and a second-round draft choice (Minnesota selected Ken Hodge Jr.) to the North Stars.

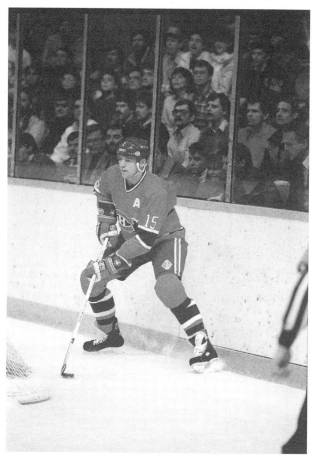

Centre Bobby Smith recorded 482 points in 505 games with Montreal.

45) Montreal sent Greg Paslawski and Gilbert Delorme to St. Louis and received Perry Turnbull in exchange.

46) Patrick Roy

47) Shayne Corson was selected eighth overall in the first round and Stephane Richer was chosen 29th overall in the second round.

48) Lucien DeBlois

49) Jose Charbonneau

50) Montreal received Russ Courtnall in return for John Kordic.

51) Denis Savard

52) Sylvain Turgeon

53) Gerald Diduck

54) Valeri Bure

Defenceman Craig Ludwig (#17) played in 597 career games as a Canadien.

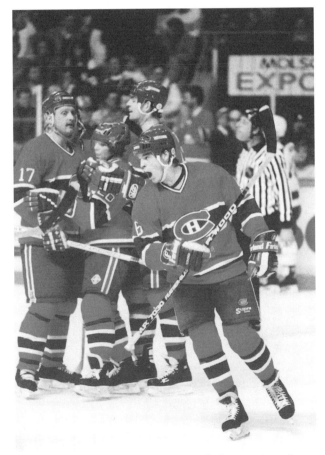

Russ Courtnall's (#6) career was revived after a trade to the Montreal Canadiens.

55) Kirk Muller and Roland Melanson

56) Kevin Haller

57) Montreal sent Shayne Corson, Brent Gilchrist and Vladimir Vujtek to Edmonton.

58) Russ Courtnall

59) Sylvain Lefebvre

60) Montreal received Gary Leeman in return for Brian Skrudland.

61) Jim Montgomery, who played in five games for Montreal before they placed him on waivers and he was claimed by Philadelphia.

62) The Canadiens dealt John LeClair, Eric Desjardins and Gilbert Dionne to the Flyers.

63) Montreal sent Mathieu Schneider, Kirk Muller and Craig Darby to the Islanders.

64) Stephane Quintal

65) Martin Rucinsky, Andrei Kovalenko and Jocelyn Thibault

66) Stephane Richer

67) Shayne Corson and Murray Baron

68) Jassen Cullimore

69) Murray Baron and Chris Murray

70) Patrick Poulin, Igor Ulanov and Mick Vukota

71) Jeff Hackett, Eric Weinrich and Alain Nasreddine

72) Trevor Linden

73) Sheldon Souray

74) The Canadiens sent Trevor Linden and Dainius Zubrus to Washington. Jan Bulis was the other player Montreal received in the deal, and they

The Canadiens paid a high price to acquire Trevor Linden, but he would only play in 107 games for Montreal, recording 63 points (25 goals).

selected Alexander Perezhogin 25th overall in 2001.

75) Shaun Van Allen came to Montreal along with Audette, while Martin Rucinsky and Benoit Brunet went to Dallas.

76) Sergei Berezin

77) Goaltender Jeff Hackett

78) Montreal acquired Alexei Kovalev in exchange for Jozef Balej and a second-round draft choice in 2004.

79) Jim Dowd

80) Centre Radek Bonk and goaltender Cristobal Huet

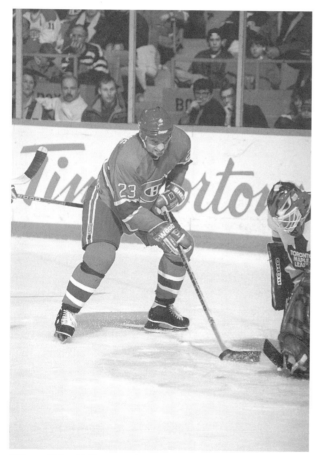

Winger Brian Bellows made a strong contribution to the Canadiens Stanley Cup win of 1993 with 15 points in 18 games.

4
Remember Him?

1) The first-ever coach of the Montreal Canadiens (he guided the team during the 1909–10 season) was a playing coach who scored three goals in 11 games. He also played on the Habs' first Stanley Cup–winning team in 1916, and was with them for one NHL season (1917–18) before he retired. He is a Hall of Fame member. Can you name him?

Pit Lepine had 241 points in 526 games with the Canadiens.

2) One of the Canadiens' first stars during their days in the National Hockey Association (NHA), this native of Valleyfield, Quebec, played defence and right wing. In 1915–16, he led the NHA in scoring with 39 points in 24 games, then starred in the playoffs (four goals in five games) as the Canadiens beat the Portland Rosebuds to win the Stanley Cup. He is a member of the Hall of Fame. Who is he?

3) Signed as a free agent in November of 1925, this centre came to prominence during the 1929–30 season, when he scored 24 goals before adding four points in six playoff games as Montreal won the Stanley Cup. In 1930–31, his regular-season output dropped to 17 goals, but he was strong in the postseason, contributing four goals in 10 games as Montreal defeated Chicago for the Cup. He played with Montreal until 1937–38, then coached the Canadiens for one year in 1939–40. Can you name this longtime Hab?

4) A native of Ottawa, Ontario, this right winger led the Montreal Canadiens in goals and points scored for two consecutive seasons (in 1922–23, when he had 23 goals and 27 points, and 1923–24, when he had 16 goals and 22 points). He was very good in the '24 playoffs, when he had five goals in four

John Quilty (left) sits with teammate Elmer Lach.

games to help Montreal take the Stanley Cup by beating the Calgary Tigers. He also played for the Boston Bruins and New York Americans. Can you name him?

5) This right winger first joined the Canadiens for the 1945–46 season, and he contributed 11 goals in 47 regular-season games. He added three goals in nine playoff games as the Canadiens won the Stanley Cup. After another 11-goal season, he was dealt to Boston early in 1947–48. He won two more

Cups as a member of the Detroit Red Wings (in 1950 and 1954). His son played in the NHL as well. Who is he?

6) Nicknamed "Pig Iron," this tough defence-man was a member of the Canadiens' first Stanley Cup–winning team in 1916. He also led the Habs in penalty minutes two years running (in 1919–20, when he had 65, and 1920–21, when he spent 85 minutes in the sin bin). He went on to play for Hamilton and Toronto, and twice led the NHL in penalty

minutes. Who was this rough-playing blueliner?

7) A smallish (5'8", 158 pounds) right winger, this native of Sorel, Quebec, became a member of the Canadiens in 1925–26. He was a double-digit goal scorer in four of his seasons with the Habs (posting a career high of 18 in 1931–32) and was on the Stanley Cup–winning teams of 1930 and 1931. In 1934–35, he tied for the team lead in assists

with 19, but in December 1935 he was dealt to Chicago, where he played for two seasons. Can you name him?

8) This Hall of Fame defenceman was born in Montreal and first played for the Canadiens in 1923–24. All but four games of his NHL career was spent in a Habs uniform. He won three Stanley Cups (in 1924, 1930 and 1931) with the Canadiens and enjoyed his best year with the team in 1929–30, when he had 13

Left winger Calum MacKay (middle of photo) played in 231 career games with Montreal between 1949 and 1955.

Ed Mazur (middle of photo) of Montreal tries to escape the clutches of Toronto netminder Harry Lumley and forward Ted Kennedy.

goals and 24 points while leading the team with 108 penalty minutes. He finished his career with Boston in 1936–37. His brother was a Montreal teammate for many seasons. Can you name him?

9) Signed as a free agent by the Canadiens in 1941, this native of Montreal was with the Habs for only two full seasons. The right winger had a great season in 1943–44, when he scored 28 goals and 44 points. He added three more points in seven playoff games as

Montreal won the Stanley Cup. He finished his career with the Montreal Royals of the Quebec Senior Hockey League (QSHL). Can you name him?

10) On June 7, 1940, this right winger joined the Montreal Canadiens in a deal with the Toronto Maple Leafs, who received the rights to Frank Eddols. The native of St. Albert, Alberta, did quite well for the Habs in his first three seasons, scoring 16, 20 and 30 goals (and leading the team in his second and third

Defenceman Emile "Butch" Bouchard was named captain of the Habs in 1948.

years). He left the club for military service during World War II, then returned for the 1945–46 season, scoring nine goals in 39 games during the regular season. He finished his NHL career after playing nine more games the following year. Who is he?

11) In its first three seasons (1917–18 through 1919–20), the NHL had five different teams comprise the circuit: the Toronto Arenas/St. Patricks, Ottawa Senators, Montreal Wanderers, Montreal Canadiens and Quebec Bulldogs. Only one player spent time with all of these original NHL franchises. A Montreal native, this defenceman was a Canadien for parts of three seasons, with his last appearance coming in 1925–26. Can you name him?

12) This defenceman from North Bay, Ontario, played his first three NHL seasons with the Montreal Canadiens. In 1920–21, he was loaned to the Hamilton Tigers, with whom he promptly led the league in penalty minutes (95). He returned to the Habs the following year and helped them to a Stanley Cup in 1924. He was traded to the Boston Bruins in 1926 and spent one season with them before wrapping up his pro career in the minors. Can you name him?

13) Many players were signed as free agents in the early '40s as teams scrambled to replace regulars who were serving in the military during World War II. The Canadiens signed one such centre in October of 1940, and the Ottawa, Ontario, native led the team in goals scored (18) and points (34) in 1940–41. His play was recognized with the Calder Trophy as the NHL's top rookie. Despite the good start, his stay in Montreal was rather short. He ended up being sent to the Boston Bruins, where he finished his 125-game NHL career in 1947. Who was he?

14) The Canadiens purchased this future Hall of Fame right winger from the Toronto Maple Leafs for $30,000 on October 4, 1942. Although he had enjoyed his best years in Toronto, the native of Moncton, New Brunswick, had a good year in Montreal with 28 goals and 50 points in 49 games in 1942–43. It was his final year in the NHL, he entered the service, then finished his playing days with various senior teams in the Maritimes. Who is he?

15) A longtime senior hockey player, this defenceman first joined the Canadiens for the 1943 playoffs, getting into five postseason games. He played the entire 1943–44 season with Montreal, registering seven goals and 17 assists and leading the NHL in penalty minutes with 98. He played in eight playoff games that year, recording three points as the Habs won the Stanley Cup. It was his only full year in the league; his pro career ended in the minors, largely with Buffalo. His son, who shared his first name, would later play in the NHL, also as a defenceman. Can you name him?

16) This native of Montreal had been a longtime member of the New York Rangers (including the Stanley Cup championship squad of 1940) before he was loaned to the Habs for one season in 1943–44. The centre/right winger had a good year with Montreal, scoring 17 goals and totalling 49 points in 44 games. He then added eight points in nine playoff games and saw his name engraved on the Cup for the second time in his career. He went back to New York for three more years, and later tried coaching the Rangers—without much success. Who was he?

17) Although he was born in Shawville, Quebec, this left winger was a member of the Toronto Maple Leafs for the first three years of his career. The Canadiens purchased him for $7,500 in May of 1940, and he spent the 1940–41 season with them. He started the next season with Montreal, then was loaned to Brooklyn and Boston before he returned on a full-time basis to the Habs in 1943–44. He scored 15 goals and totalled 47 points in 47 games in '43–44 before helping Montreal win the Stanley Cup with five goals and three assists in nine playoff games. He won another Cup in 1946 and finished his career with the Habs in 1948–49. Can you name him?

18) Known as "Spider," this native of Winnipeg joined the Montreal Canadiens for two

Defenceman Bob Turner (right) poses with fellow blueliners Tom Johnson (centre) and Jean Guy Talbot (left).

Montreal defenceman Al Langlois (#19) is watched by Detroit's Marcel Pronovost.

games during the 1951 playoffs after playing minor-pro hockey in western Canada. He was a playoff call-up again in 1952 and 1953, contributing to a Stanley Cup victory in the latter season with two goals and two assists in seven games. He played a full season in 1953–54, scoring seven times and totalling 21 points in 67 games. He played part of one more season in Montreal before going to Chicago briefly in 1956–57. He then returned to the minors for a number of years before retiring. Can you name him?

19) Born in Quebec City in 1929, this centre played minor-league hockey before the Canadiens picked up his rights for the 1954–55 season. He had 11 goals and 33 points in 59 games in his first year in the NHL, and although his totals dropped after that, he was still a valued member of the Stanley Cup teams of 1956 and 1957. The '56–57 season was

his last in the NHL; he returned to the minors with the Quebec Aces and Charlotte Checkers, among other teams, before retiring in 1968. Can you name him?

20) After George Hainsworth and Lorne Chabot were traded away, the Canadiens turned over the netminding duties to a goalie they had originally picked up in a cash deal with the Philadelphia Quakers. This netminder split the 1933–34 season between Montreal and Detroit (to whom he was loaned for 30 games), leading the league with a 1.47 goals-against average. He was never again as good with Montreal, but he did post a couple of winning seasons (22–17–5 in 1936–37 and 18–17–12 in 1937–38) and was a two-time second-team All-Star. He left the Habs after three games in 1940–41. Can you name him?

21) In 1926, Montreal purchased the rights to a Calgary Tigers defenceman who had been one of the major stars of the Western Canada Hockey League. In his first season as a Hab (1926–27), he earned the Hart Trophy as the league's most valuable player—becoming the first Canadien to win the award—after scoring six goals and six assists in 44 games. He played one more full season before a brief stay in Chicago. He then became a minor leaguer with two teams in Philadelphia before retiring in 1936. He was later elected to the Hall of Fame. Who was he?

22) Before Bill Durnan became a star goaltender for the Canadiens, the team had employed a Montreal native in net for a little over a couple of seasons. His best year with the Canadiens came in 1942–43, when he played in a league-high 50 contests and posted a

19–19–12 record. When Durnan was ready to take over, this netminder was loaned to the Toronto Maple Leafs, with whom he earned a place on the NHL's second All-Star team in 1944. He then was shipped to Boston for two seasons before a return to Montreal for 10 games in 1945–46, when he filled in for an injured Durnan. He finished his NHL career with one season in Chicago. Who was he?

23) This tall (6'1"), rangy right winger joined the Montreal Canadiens after a good junior career with the Regina Pats. He joined the Habs for five games between 1952 and 1954, then played in 29 games for the team in 1954–55, scoring seven goals before he was sent to Chicago to finish the season (under a plan by which the other five NHL teams helped bail out the floundering Blackhawks). He ended up winning the Calder Trophy and was still in Chicago when they won the Stanley Cup in 1961. He won three more Cups with the Maple Leafs before he retired. Who was this unusual rookie of the year?

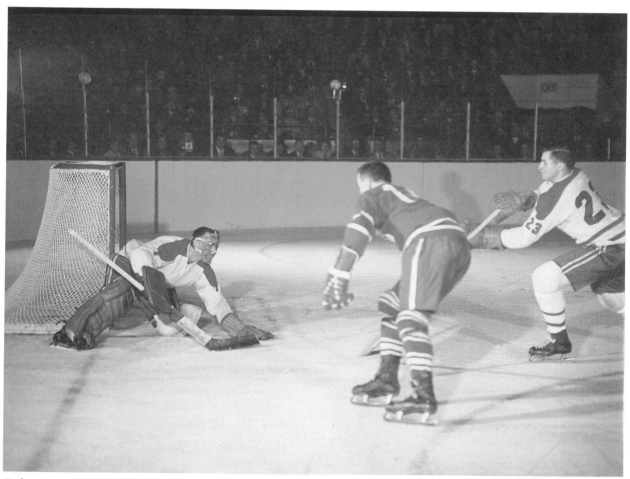

Defenceman Al MacNeil (#23) tries to keep Dave Keon of Toronto away from goalie Jacques Plante.

24) Known by his nickname of "Busher," this right winger was born in Chapleau, Ontario, in 1925 and spent his entire 601-game NHL career with the Canadiens. He was a four-time Stanley Cup winner (1953, 1956, 1957 and 1958) whose best year as a Hab was in 1951–52, when he scored 20 times. He was a good playoff performer, with 23 goals and 40 points in 91 post-season games. In the '56 playoffs he produced 12 points (including eight goals) in 12 games. Who was he?

25) A two-time second-team All-Star (1945 and 1949), this defenceman from Holland, Manitoba, played his entire NHL career (425 games) with the Canadiens. He joined the Habs in 1942–43 after playing junior hockey in Winnipeg, and he played on two Stanley Cup winners (in 1944 and 1946). He had a bit of a scoring touch, having netted 50 career goals, including a high of 10 in 1947–48. His final NHL season was in 1950–51, after which he played senior hockey in Montreal with the Royals. Can you name him?

26) A native of Montreal, this Hall of Fame defenceman did not learn to skate until he was 16 years old and in high school! But after playing junior hockey in Verdun, he caught the eye of the Canadiens and their new coach, Dick Irvin. The rugged blueliner made the Habs in 1941–42 and would win four Stanley Cups (1944, 1946, 1953 and 1956) with the team. He played his entire NHL career (785 games) as a Hab, and was team captain between 1948 and 1956. Who was he?

27) One of the top defencemen of his time, this native of Winnipeg joined the Montreal Canadiens in 1940–41 and earned five All-Star team selections (two on the first team). He recorded more than 100 penalty minutes three times in his 341-game career, which was played entirely for the Canadiens. After his Hall of Fame career ended in 1949–50, he became an important executive in the Montreal organization for many years. Who was he?

28) The Canadiens claimed this native of Montreal from the Boston Bruins organization in June of 1957. The burly right winger (5'10", 170 pounds) had started his career with Detroit, winning a Stanley Cup with the Red Wings in 1955, and had spent just one season in Boston. He won three more Cups with Montreal (1958, 1959 and 1960) before finishing his career a couple of years later. His most productive season as a goal scorer was in 1959–60, when he scored 17; the previous spring, he had led all playoff goal getters with 10 (in 11 games). He was also known for wrestling bears in the off-season! Who was he?

29) Montreal picked up this left winger from Detroit in a 1949 trade for Joe Carveth. He scored eight times in 52 games for the Habs in 1949–50, and followed that up with a career-high 18 goals in 1950–51. He bounced between the Habs and their farm team in Buffalo, but he was around for the post-season (four points in seven games) when the Canadiens won the Stanley Cup in 1953. He played two more years with the Habs (including a 14-goal, 35-point effort in 50 games in his final year of 1954–55) before going on to play senior hockey for one more season. Can you name him?

30) A smallish centre at 5'8" and 160 pounds, this Montreal native played junior hockey in the area and then saw senior action in Cincinnati and Shawinigan before joining the Habs in 1955–56. He played a grand total of six regular-season games (two goals) and seven in the playoffs (no goals, one assist), yet he was on two Stanley Cup teams (1957 and 1958) with Montreal! He was also a member of the famed Whitby Dunlops, who won the world amateur hockey championship in 1958. Can you name him?

31) This native of Shawingan Falls, Quebec, played his junior hockey in Montreal before joining the Canadiens for his first NHL season in 1956–57. The left winger won the Stanley Cup in each of his first four seasons in the league and had his best year as a Hab in 1957–58, when he potted 18 goals. His highest point total was 31 in 1959–60, but the next season saw him dealt to Boston for Jean-Guy Gendron. He also played for Detroit and saw his last NHL action (eight games) with the Minnesota North Stars in 1967–68. Who was he?

32) A sturdy (5'11", 175 pounds) defenceman, this native of Verdun, Quebec, played in 652 NHL games, starting with a three-game stint as a Hab in 1950–51. He played in 40 games for Montreal the next year, before becoming a regular in the team's Stanley Cup season of 1952–53. He stayed with the Canadiens for another five years (earning three more Cups) and recorded a career-best 23 points in 1957–58. He was then dealt to the Chicago Blackhawks, where he played for four more seasons, winning another Cup in 1961. He played his last year of

hockey for the Quebec Aces. Can you name him?

33) This defenceman from Regina joined the Habs for the 1955–56 season and was one of the group of players who played on all five of their Stanley Cup–winning teams between 1956 and 1960. His best year in Montreal was in 1958–59, when he had four goals and 24 assists in 68 appearances, but his totals dropped the next year to no goals and nine assists in 54 games. He was sent to Chicago in 1961 in exchange for Fred Hilts and played two seasons for the Blackhawks before spending one more year in the minors with Buffalo. Can you name him?

34) A large (6', 205 pounds) blueliner from Magog, Quebec, first joined the Habs for seven games in the 1958 playoffs (after only one regular-season appearance) and earned a spot on a Stanley Cup–winning team. He won two more Cups with Montreal, and while he scored only two goals as a Hab, he was usually in double digits in the assists column. He was traded to the New York Rangers in June of 1961, where he was reunited with former teammate Doug Harvey. He later played for Detroit and Boston. He was often called "Junior." Can you name him?

35) A two-time NHL All-Star (including one selection to the first team) during his time with the Montreal Canadiens, this native of Baldur, Manitoba, debuted with the Habs during the 1947–48 season, making one appearance. He won six Stanley Cups with Montreal and recorded 10 or more assists in nine seasons while playing defence. His best

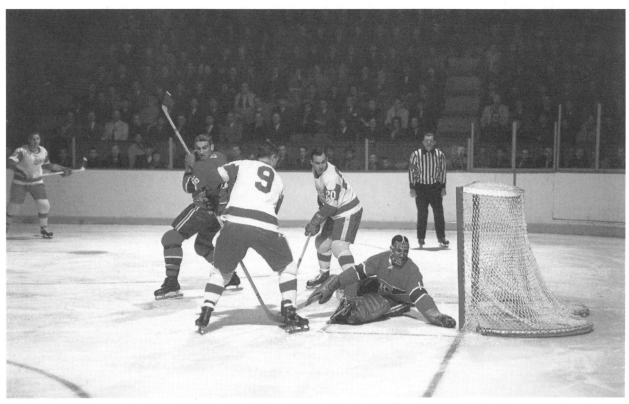

Rugged defenceman Lou Fontinato (#19) has Gordie Howe (#9) and Parker MacDonald (#20) of Detroit to worry about in front of goalie Jacques Plante.

year with the team was in 1959–60, when he scored 10 goals and added 29 assists. He was claimed by Boston in the waiver draft in June of 1963 and played two seasons for the Bruins before retiring. He became an executive and coach with the Bruins, winning one Cup with them in 1972. Who is he?

36) Born in Sydney, Nova Scotia, in 1935, this journeyman defenceman played only one season for the Canadiens. He started his career with the Toronto Maple Leafs but was traded to Montreal in June of 1960. The blue-liner became a regular with the Canadiens in 1961–62, when he played in 61 games (one goal and eight assists), but was traded to

Chicago for Wayne Hicks before the start of the next season. He was a Blackhawk for four seasons before going to the New York Rangers for a year and logging one last NHL season with the Pittsburgh Penguins. He later coached the Habs to a surprise Stanley Cup win in 1971. Who was he?

37) In 1962–63, this native of Montreal played 65 games for the Canadiens and recorded a career-high 18 points (one goal, 17 assists). A year later, however, he was back in the minors for all but one game. The 1964–65 campaign saw the blueliner appear in two playoff games for the Habs, which got his name on the Stanley Cup when Montreal

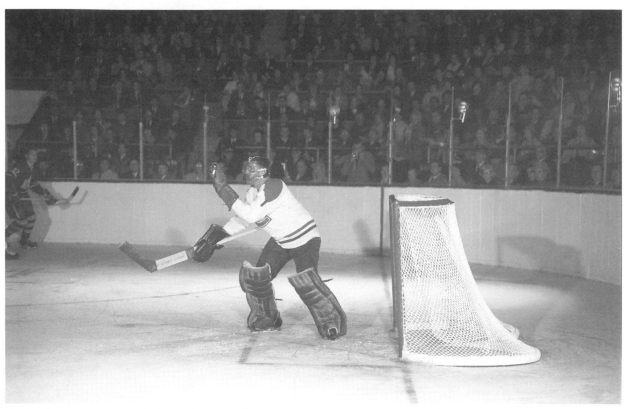

Goaltender Cesare Maniago (#1) posted a 3.07 goals against average in 14 games as a Canadien.

knocked off Chicago in the finals. He became an original member of the Philadelphia Flyers, playing in 65 games for the expansion club and recording a career-best five goals. He played briefly for Boston before ending his 166-game NHL career with Montreal in 1969–70. Who was he?

38) A longtime minor leaguer, this left winger played in a total of nine regular-season games for the Canadiens (four in 1956–57 and five in 1957–58), registering three points, all of them assists. He scored his only goal in a Montreal uniform during the 1957 All-Star Game, which the Habs lost 5–3 to the NHL All-Stars. He was dealt to Toronto in 1960,

but played exclusively for the Leafs' farm club, the Rochester Americans. His son, John, made it to the NHL with the St. Louis Blues and the Quebec Nordiques. Can you name him?

39) One of the most prolific minor-league goal scorers in hockey history, this native of Dolbeau, Quebec, was known as "Boom Boom." He scored 77 goals in 1963–64 for the St. Louis Braves of the Central Professional Hockey League, but never got a chance at a steady NHL job until the Oakland Seals joined the league in 1967–68. He scored nine goals in 58 contests, then got to play in two games for the Canadiens in 1968–69 (scoring

no points) after he was included in a multi-player deal. He was soon back in the minors, but he played with the Quebec Nordiques for their first three seasons in the World Hockey Association. Can you name him?

40) During the mid-'60s, the Montreal Canadiens had two defencemen, both with the first name of Noel, play on a Stanley Cup winner. One was with the 1965 champions, appearing in 16 regular-season games and three in the playoffs, while the other played on the 1966 Cup winners (15 regular-season games and three in the playoffs). Both went on to play for expansion teams and found themselves as teammates on the 1972–73 Atlanta Flames during that team's first year in the NHL. Can you name both players?

41) Acquired in a deal with the New York Rangers in 1961, this rough-and-tumble defenceman twice led the Canadiens in penalty minutes during his two-year stay (his 167 minutes in just 54 games in 1961–62 also led the league). His career was abruptly ended when he suffered a serious neck injury during a game against the Rangers at the Forum on March 9, 1963. Although he recovered from his injury, he was not able to resume his NHL career, which lasted 535 games and saw him rack up 1,247 penalty minutes. Who was he?

42) A native of Cap de la Madeleine, Quebec, this right winger began his NHL career with the New York Rangers in 1960–61, but he bounced back and forth between the big league and the minors—even after he was acquired by the Canadiens in a 1963 deal. He was with Montreal in 1966 when they won the Stanley Cup, contributing a goal and an assist in four appearances in the post-season. He moved to Philadelphia for the 1967–68 season and scored 21 goals for the first-year club. In 1969 he was sent to Los Angeles, and he returned to Montreal in 1970–71. He played in 10 playoff games that year to earn another Cup. He also played for Detroit, Atlanta and Vancouver before retiring. Can you name him?

43) After a stellar junior career with the Montreal Junior Canadiens (135 points in his final year), this native of Montreal joined the Habs for four games (scoring once) in 1963–64. A small (5'8", 165 pounds) left winger, he had difficulty breaking into the NHL during the last years of the "Original Six" but caught a big break with expansion. He joined the Minnesota North Stars in 1967–68, scoring 18 times in 74 games. He also played for Chicago and St. Louis, but had his best years with the Vancouver Canucks, whom he led in scoring in four of his six seasons with the team. Can you name him?

44) One of the best two-way players ever to play for the Canadiens, this left winger joined the Habs in 1960–61, recording 18 points in 45 games. He would play his entire career (509 games) with the Canadiens and would record 20 or more goals in five seasons. His best year came in 1961–62, his first full year with the team, when he scored 32 goals. Health issues forced him to retire, but not before he had won three Stanley Cups. He became a television broadcaster and was elected to the Hall of Fame in the media wing. Can you name him?

45) One of the first tall (6'3") netminders to make his mark in the NHL, this native of Trail, British Columbia, started his career with the Toronto Maple Leafs in 1960–61. The Habs picked him up from Toronto's Rochester farm club in the inter-league draft in 1961, and he played in 14 games, posting a 5–5–4 record during the 1961–62 season. He then played in the minors until a trade to New York in 1965, but spent most of his career (1967–1978) as a Minnesota North Star. He finished up with the Vancouver Canucks, posting a career record of 189–259–96, but is perhaps best known for giving up milestone goals to Bernie Geoffrion, Bobby Hull and Stan Mikita. Can you name him?

46) Not only was this centre unusual because he wore a helmet, he was also one of the first U.S. college graduates (University of Michigan) to play in the NHL. The native of Regina joined the Canadiens for four games in 1961–62, then made 37 appearances the following year. He played in 69 games in 1963–64 and had 16 points, and was with the team when it reclaimed the Stanley Cup in 1965. He was sent to the New York Rangers in 1966, but did not blossom as an NHL player until he joined the St. Louis Blues. A good playmaker and scorer when he was on top of his game, he enjoyed four top-notch years with the Blues, including a six-goal game against the Philadelphia Flyers. He also played for Detroit and finished with 261 goals and 658 points. Who was he?

Red Berenson (#23, with helmet) scored 14 goals and added 23 assists during his stay in Montreal.

47) A veteran of many NHL campaigns, this native of Kirkland Lake, Ontario, joined the Montreal Canadiens for 25 regular-season games (recording no goals and five assists) and one more contest in the playoffs in 1967–68, giving the journeyman defenceman yet another Stanley Cup win—he had won previous championships with Detroit (1955) and Toronto (1964 and 1967). His 790-game NHL career also took him to Boston, Minnesota, Philadelphia, Los Angeles and Buffalo before he retired. Can you name this well-travelled blueliner?

48) Considered a top prospect after playing junior hockey in his hometown of Montreal, this big defenceman (6'1", 185 pounds) would play in a total of 42 games for the Canadiens over parts of two seasons before moving on to the Oakland Seals in the 1968 intra-league draft. The high-scoring reaguard was on the Canadiens' Stanley Cup-winning team of 1968 (getting into one playoff game) and was on another Cup champion with Boston in 1972. He was part of a 1975 blockbuster trade between the Bruins and New York Rangers, and ended up playing in 1,087 regular-season games before retiring. Who is he?

49) One of three brothers to play in the NHL, this centre from Noranda, Quebec, played for the Montreal Junior Canadiens before joining the Habs for 13 games in 1968–69 (contributing one goal and three assists). He added a goal in the playoffs as the Canadiens won their second straight Stanley Cup, but played only one more season for Montreal before he was sold to the St. Louis Blues. He had 21 goals and 53 for the Blues in 1970–71, but jumped to Winnipeg of the World

Hockey Association two years later. His brother J.P. (short for Jean-Pierre) played for the Chicago Blackhawks (519 career games), while his other sibling, Paulin, was a Vancouver Canuck for his entire 183-game NHL career. Can you name him?

50) This right winger was born in Malartic, Quebec, in 1947 and played some of his junior hockey for the Montreal Junior Canadiens. He turned pro with Montreal's farm team, the Houston Apollos, where he spent three seasons before being called up for the 1969 playoffs. He appeared in two games (scoring no points) as the Habs won the Stanley Cup. He stayed with Montreal for 23 games (two goals, three assists) in 1969–70, but logged the rest of the season in the minors with the Nova Scotia Voyageurs. He was dealt along with Larry Mickey to the Los Angeles Kings in return for Leon Rochefort, Gregg Boddy and Wayne Thomas on May 22, 1970. Who was he?

51) A small (5'7", 155 pounds) but speedy left winger, this native of Weymouth, Massachusetts, became the first U.S.-born player to get his name on the Stanley Cup since goaltender Frank Brimsek (with Boston in 1941), when the Canadiens won the championship in 1971. He first became a member of the Habs in 1969–70 when he played in 16 games, scoring two goals and an assist, then appeared in 29 games in 1970–71, scoring six times and adding five assists. He had no points in six playoff games, but caught the eye of the California Golden Seals, who acquired him in a cash deal. He also played for Chicago, Detroit, New York Rangers, Colorado Rockies and Los Angeles before his

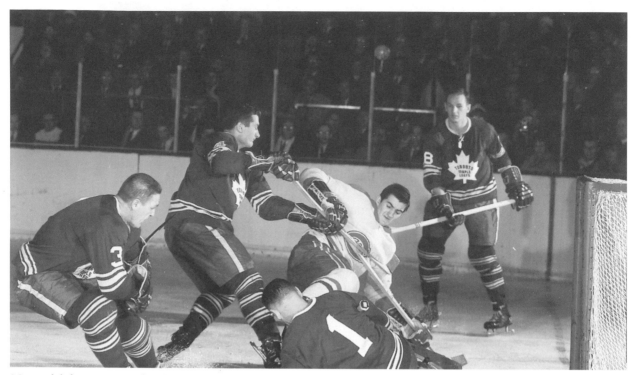

Montreal defenceman Carol Vadnais (#17) tries to avoid running over Toronto goalie Johnny Bower (#1).

310-game NHL career was over. Can you name him?

52) This Quebec-born netminder played the last two years of his junior career with Niagara Falls before joining the Houston Apollos of the Central Hockey League in 1968–69. He enjoyed a good season there, posting a 24–19–10 record in 53 games, which earned him a 10-game stint with the Canadiens the following year. He posted a 4–3–2 mark in a season that also saw him play for the Habs' American Hockey League affiliate, the Montreal Voyageurs. In 1970–71, he got into 30 games (13–11–4), but was pushed aside when Ken Dryden joined the team for the playoffs. He was rescued by the expansion Atlanta Flames, who selected him in the 1972 expansion draft, and he stayed with them for over five seasons. He also played for Philadelphia, Colorado and Buffalo, finishing his career with a 149–198–76 record with 14 shutouts. Can you name him?

53) A native of Sundridge, Ontario, this right winger was unable to break out of Montreal's farm system (he played in a total of nine regular-season games for the Habs in 1964–65, logging three assists) until expansion came along and the Pittsburgh Penguins claimed his rights. He had four good years in Pittsburgh (recording 25- and 21-goal seasons) before Atlanta claimed him in the 1972 expansion draft. He was named the first captain of the Flames and scored 20 goals during the 1972–73 season. Who was he?

54) The St. Louis Blues have had 10 general managers in their history to date, and only one of them played for the Montreal Canadiens. This native of Lynn, Massachusetts, played in parts of three seasons for the Habs (between 1969 and 1972), scoring nine goals and 24 assists in 94 career games. He is perhaps best known as the first player signed by the New England Whalers of the World Hockey Association in 1972. He enjoyed a few very good seasons during his seven years with the Whalers. Can you name him?

55) Acquired in a deal with St. Louis in June of 1974, this feisty left winger joined the Canadiens for 63 games in 1974–75, during which he scored six goals and totalled 16 points. Prior to donning the Habs' famed sweater, he had played for Boston, Pittsburgh and the New York Rangers. The native of High River, Alberta, went on to play for Minnesota before jumping to Edmonton of the WHA. After retiring, he made his mark on the game as a coach and general manager. Who is he?

56) This right winger/defenceman had one of the most interesting careers in the history of the Canadiens. The native of Toronto had two very distinct stints tenures the Habs, the first coming in the mid-'60s, when he won a couple of Stanley Cups (1965 and '66). He then joined the expansion St. Louis Blues in 1967–68, scoring a career-high 14 goals and 37 points. Five years later he was re-acquired by the Canadiens, and he played on two more Cup teams (1976 and 1977) before going back to the Blues for one more year. He was one of the NHL's best role players, and his

Montreal career numbers show 63 goals and 100 assists in 611 games. He later tried his hand at coaching with Buffalo, Hartford and St. Louis. Who was he?

57) It's never easy to follow in the footsteps of a famous father, especially one who played for the Canadiens, but this large defenceman (6'2", 205 pounds) did very well during his time with the Habs and was part of five Stanley Cup–winning teams (1971, '73, '76, '77 and '78). Given his size, he was expected to be a physical force, but he was more of a gentle giant, fighting only when it was necessary to do so (although few would challenge him). He scored 16 goals and 82 points in 489 games as a Hab, but his career in Montreal came to an end after he lost a celebrated fight to Stan Jonathan of the Boston Bruins in the 1978 playoffs. He went on to play for the Washington Capitals. Who was he?

58) A longtime member of the Boston Bruins and a player on Team Canada in the 1972 Summit Series, this defenceman joined the Montreal Canadiens in a 1974 deal with the St. Louis Blues. He won two Stanley Cups with the Bruins (1970 and 1972), and although he played in 76 games for the Habs in 1975–76 (recording 12 assists), he did not play in a single playoff game that year. He was sent to the Pittsburgh Penguins for a third-round draft choice, and he also played for the New York Rangers and Colorado Rockies. Who was he?

59) Drafted 14th overall by the Canadiens in 1972, this defenceman began his pro career with the Nova Scotia Voyageurs of the American Hockey League, with whom he spent most of

his first three years. He made it into 29 games for the Canadiens between 1973 and 1975, then played in 46 games for Montreal, registering six goals and 11 assists in 1975–76; although the Habs took back the Stanley Cup that spring, he did not take part in any playoff games. He was dealt to the Colorado Rockies for a third-round choice in November of '76 and was later traded to Buffalo for Rene Robert. He also played for the Quebec Nordiques and finished with 274 assists and 358 points in 588 career games. Can you name him?

60) One of the nicknames this incredibly tall (6'6") defenceman went by was "Towering Inferno" (after a disaster movie of the time). Selected 33rd overall by the Canadiens in 1974, he led the Canadiens in penalty minutes for three straight seasons (1977–78 to 1979–80) and was on two Stanley Cup–winning teams (1977 and 1978). He was dealt to Pittsburgh for a draft choice in 1980, and he also played for the Hartford Whalers. He later became a player agent. Who is he?

61) Montreal signed this free-agent goaltender in 1967 after he completed his college career at Michigan Tech. The native of Sault Ste. Marie, Ontario, played the 1967–68 season

Canadiens goaltender Phil Myre tries to stop Ron Ellis of the Maple Leafs in close.

with the Vancouver Canucks of the Western Hockey League, winning 25 of his league-leading 63 games played. He spent part of the 1968–69 season with the Montreal Canadiens, getting into 13 contests and posting a 5–4–4 record with two shutouts, but he was declared surplus to the Habs' needs and was claimed by the Chicago Blackhawks in the intra-league draft of 1969. He played the rest of his career with Chicago, and was voted into the Hall of Fame after winning a total of 423 games. Can you name him?

62) After a career with the University of Notre Dame, this native of Washington, D.C., joined the Nova Scotia Voyageurs of the AHL for the 1974–75 season. The next year saw him split his time between the Voyageurs and the Canadiens (for 19 regular-season games and 13 more in the play-offs that saw Montreal win the Stanley Cup). He played in 72 and 74 games over the next two years, winning two more Cups in 1977 and '78. He retired from the game for two years, but returned to play one season for the Minnesota North Stars. He scored 12 goals and 63 assists in his 207-game career and was elected to the United States Hockey Hall of Fame. Who was he?

63) A graduate of the University of Minnesota, this defenceman made his debut with the Canadiens during the 1977 playoffs, when he got into five games and Montreal took the Stanley Cup. He spent most of his time in the Montreal organization with the Nova Scotia Voyageurs, appearing in only one regular-

Jimmy Roberts wore sweater numbers 26 and 6 during his career with the Canadiens.

season game with the Habs (in 1977–78). The North Stars signed the native of Hibbing, Minnesota, as a free agent in 1978, and he played three seasons in his home state. Can you name him?

64) This speedy winger, who had enjoyed a stellar junior career with the Toronto Marlboros, was selected 10th overall by the Canadiens in the 1977 Amateur Draft. He played in the World Hockey Association for his first three years as a pro, joining the Canadiens for the 1978–79 season, during

which he scored 11 goals and 31 points in 54 regular-season games. He added three goals and five points in 12 playoff games, helping the Habs to a Stanley Cup win. He hit his stride with a 35-goal season in 1980–81, then put together back-to-back 40-goal years, but was traded to Minnesota in 1983. He won another Stanley Cup in Edmonton and also played for the Buffalo Sabres. Who was he?

65) This big (6'2", 200 pounds) right winger from Winnipeg was chosen fifth overall by the

Defenceman Don Awrey was acquired in a deal with St. Louis for Chuck Lefley.

Montreal Canadiens in the 1974 Amateur Draft. He went on to play only 23 games for the Habs (all during the 1978–79 season), scoring a goal and three assists. He scored only one goal in eight playoff games in '78, but it was an important overtime marker that beat Toronto in overtime at Maple Leaf Gardens. After helping the Habs win the Stanley Cup, he moved to Edmonton and then to the New York Rangers, where he finished his 89-game NHL career. Who was he?

66) Montreal drafted this native of Calgary, Alberta, 52nd overall in the 1975 Amateur Draft. The 6'1", 180-pound right winger played at the University of Michigan before joining the Nova Scotia Voyageurs of the AHL for some seasoning. In 1978–79 he played in 41 games for the Canadiens (scoring nine goals and eight assists). He contributed four points, including a goal, in eight play-off games and won his first Stanley Cup. The Pittsburgh Penguins acquired him in a deal before the start of the next season, but he had his best days after a 1981 trade to the Edmonton Oilers. He posted three straight seasons of 24 or more goals in Edmonton (including a five-goal game) and won two more Cups. Who was he?

67) The Canadiens drafted this native of Montreal, hoping he might be something like his father, who had been one of their greatest players. The 5'10", 185-pound winger was selected eighth overall in 1978 after a high-scoring junior career with the Cornwall Royals (including a 68-goal season in 1977–78). He played for the Quebec Nordiques for their last year in the WHA,

but the Habs reclaimed him prior to the 1979–80 season, during part of which his famous dad coached the team. He scored no goals in 32 games, but managed to pot 20 for the Winnipeg Jets in 1980–81. He played in only one more NHL game after that year. Can you name him?

68) When Ken Dryden retired after the Habs' 1979 Stanley Cup win, they quickly moved to fill his spot in goal by acquiring this native of Chambly, Quebec, from the Pittsburgh Penguins. He had a very good season in 1979–80, posting a rather remarkable 25–3–3 record in 34 appearances. He went 2–3 in the playoffs, however, as the four-time Stanley Cup champions were ousted by Minnesota. He played two more years in Montreal, but was never as good again. He returned to the Penguins, where he finished his NHL career with a total of 146 wins and 203 losses. Who was he?

69) Since they drafted him 166th overall in 1980, the Habs probably did not entertain high hopes for this goaltender from Ste. Foy, Quebec. After a four-game stint (all losses) with the team during the 1983–84 regular season, he became the surprise of the play-offs, posting a 9–6 record and taking the Canadiens all the way to the semi-finals before they lost to the defending Stanley Cup champion New York Islanders. He played well the next year, posting a record of 26–18–8 in 54 games, but the team bowed out of the post-season in the second round. He played in 18 games in 1985–86, but was dealt to the Winnipeg Jets when Patrick Roy came along. Who was he?

Goaltender Steve Penney (#37) had one great playoff year with Montreal.

70) A native of Sydney, Nova Scotia, this big (6'2", 210 pounds) left winger was selected 124th overall in 1980 by the Canadiens after he played U.S. college hockey for the RPI Engineers. He put up good numbers with the Nova Scotia Voyageurs for two minor-league seasons before joining the Habs on a full-time basis (playing 70 games) in 1984–85. He produced anywhere from 17 to 23 goals over the next seven seasons and was a major contributor to the Canadiens' Stanley Cup win in 1986 (seven points in 20 games). He scored 16 times in his last year with the club

Left winger Mike McPhee recorded 324 points in 581 games with Montreal.

in 11 playoff matches. The next season saw him play in only 38 games (scoring two goals and three assists), but he dressed for the last game of the 1986 finals against Calgary and got his name on the Stanley Cup. He was dealt to Winnipeg in January 1987. Can you name him?

72) After playing for the University of Wisconsin, this 6'2", 195-pound left winger was selected 33rd overall by the Canadiens in the 1982 entry draft. He joined the team for three games during the 1985–86 regular season, in which he scored no points. He made seven appearances during the '86 play-offs, in which he scored one goal (in the finals) and added three assists to the team's Cup run. He played in 46 games for the Habs the following year but was dealt to the New Jersey Devils in 1987 for a draft choice with which the Canadiens took Mathieu Schneider. Who was he?

73) The Canadiens drafted this defenceman from Minneapolis, Minnesota, 145th overall in 1981. He remained in college, delaying his debut with the team until 1984–85, when he played in 75 games, scoring 10 goals and adding 35 assists. He played in 62 games the following year, contributing seven goals and 23 assists, but he did not get into a single playoff game when Montreal won the Stanley Cup in 1986. The big (6'2", 195 pounds) but generally soft blueliner was quickly dealt to the New Jersey Devils for a second-round draft choice. The Devils later traded him to Toronto for a first-round draft choice (who turned out to be Scott Niedermayer). Can you name him?

before he was dealt to Minnesota in 1992. He finished with an even 200 career goals. Can you name this very reliable player?

71) In 1981, the Canadiens used the 88th-overall pick in the draft to claim a left winger born in Canton, Massachusetts. He spent the next four seasons at Providence College, then got his first taste of NHL action in the spring of 1985. He appeared in three regular-season games, netting his first goal as a professional, then contributed two goals and four points

74) A native of Timra, Sweden, this right winger played three seasons for the Canadiens after being drafted 82nd overall in 1981. His first year, 1985–86, was the most memorable; he set a Habs rookie record for most points in a season, tallying 32 goals and 39 assists for 71 points. Despite that debut, he did not win the Calder Trophy as rookie of the year. He was, however, a member of the '86 Stanley Cup champions, contributing five points (two goals) in 16 games played. The 1986–87 season saw him appear in only 41 games, scoring 12 goals, and after chipping in 13 goals in 48 games a year later, he returned to play in Sweden. Who was he?

75) Most teams do not expect a player drafted 231st overall to make it the NHL, but this right winger, selected by the Habs in that slot in 1978, was very determined. He made his mark as an enforcer and led the Canadiens in penalty minutes eight years in a row. However, he could also score goals, netting 21 in 1984–85 and 19 in 1985–86. In the 1986 playoffs, the native of Boston was a force to be reckoned with, racking up 141 penalty minutes and scoring one goal in 18 games as the Habs won the Stanley Cup. He was dealt to the New York Rangers and later played for his hometown Bruins as well. He returned to the Habs for his last NHL season, and brought his career totals to 110 goals scored and 225 points to go along with 3,043 penalty minutes. Can you name him?

76) Known as a blueliner with offensive skill, this native of Montreal was drafted 10th overall by the Vancouver Canucks in 1984. He was dealt to Philadelphia two years later, and the Canadiens picked him up in a 1988 deal with the Flyers. Never a big scorer at the NHL level, his highest point total with the Canadiens was 19 in 1990–91; in '92–93, he netted a career-high eight goals. Playing in 20 post-season games in 1993, he contributed four points as Montreal won the Stanley Cup. The veteran went on to play for seven more teams (making 10 in total) before his 899-game career ended. Can you name this well-travelled defender?

77) This left winger from Drummondville, Quebec, was selected 81st overall in 1990. He

Tough guy forward Chris Nilan led the NHL in penalty minutes on two occasions.

is perhaps best known for having a brother who was elected to the Hall of Fame. He made a big splash as a rookie in 1991–92, scoring 21 goals in 39 games, and he followed that up with 20 goals in 75 games in 1992–93. He was very good in the 1993 playoffs, with six goals and six assists in 20 games, helping Montreal to the Stanley Cup (a prize that eluded his legendary sibling). One more full season in Montreal saw him score 19 goals and 45 points in 74 games, but then he was included in a major deal with Philadelphia.

Gilbert Dionne was a Hab between 1990 and 1995.

He played in only 22 games as a Flyer before closing out his NHL career with a five-game stop in Florida. Who was he?

78) After playing in 66 games with the Tampa Bay Lightning during the 1992–93 season, this rugged veteran defenceman joined the Montreal Canadiens for eight games to close the regular season. He then played in seven playoff games (although none in the finals) when the Habs took the Stanley Cup. It was the second championship for the player who was selected first overall in 1979 by the Colorado Rockies and took part in 1,044 career NHL games. Who was he?

79) Signed as a free agent by the Canadiens in 1985, this native of Winnipeg went on to play 506 games as a Hab, scoring 90 goals and totalling 269 points. He was known as a grinding right winger who could play well in big games. He did some of his best work in the playoffs (34 points in 77 post-season games for Montreal) and won one Stanley Cup (1993) with the Canadiens before he was dealt in 1995 to Colorado. He was captain of the Habs for a brief time before he was traded, and he went on to win Cups with Colorado and Dallas. In 2003–04 he was still playing NHL hockey for the Vancouver Canucks. Who is he?

80) Montreal signed this free-agent centre in 2001; he registered 41 points in 70 games during the 2001–02 season, then added 10 points in 12 playoff contests. His career was defined by his play with St. Louis, Calgary and Toronto (he was captain of the Leafs for a brief time), and he won one Stanley Cup with the Flames in 1989 when they beat the

Doug Gilmour recorded 71 points (including 50 assists) in 131 games with the Canadiens.

Canadiens in the final. After 61 more games with the Habs in 2002–03, he was dealt back to Toronto. After only one more game in the blue and white, his highly productive career (1,414 points in 1,474 NHL games) was ended by a knee injury. Who is he?

Answers

Sylvio Mantha

Floyd Curry

15) Mike McMahon
16) Phil Watson
17) Murph Chamberlain
18) Eddie Mazur
19) Jackie Leclair
20) Wilf Cude
21) Herb Gardiner
22) Paul Bibeault

Jean Gauthier

Dollard St. Laurent

23) Ed Litzenberger
24) Floyd Curry
25) Glen Harmon
26) Emile "Butch" Bouchard
27) Ken Reardon
28) Marcel Bonin
29) Calum MacKay
30) Connie Broden
31) Andre Pronovost

32) Dollard St. Laurent
33) Bob Turner
34) Al Langlois
35) Tom Johnson
36) Al MacNeil
37) Jean Gauthier
38) Stan Smrke
39) Alain Caron

Christian Bordeleau

Gilles Tremblay

40) Noel Picard and Noel Price
41) Lou Fontinato
42) Leon Rochefort
43) Andre Boudrias
44) Gilles Tremblay
45) Cesare Maniago
46) Gordon "Red" Berenson
47) Larry Hillman

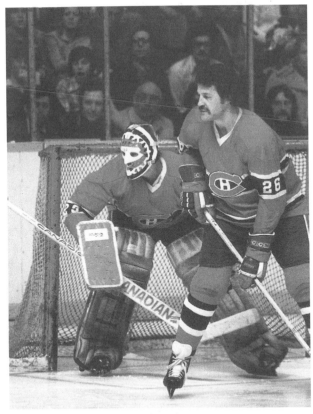

Defenceman Pierre Bouchard (#26)

48) Carol Vadnais
49) Christian Bordeleau
50) Lucien Grenier
51) Bobby Sheehan
52) Phil Myre
53) Keith McCreary
54) Larry Pleau
55) Glen Sather
56) Jimmy Roberts
57) Pierre Bouchard
58) Don Awrey
59) John Van Boxmeer
60) Gilles Lupien

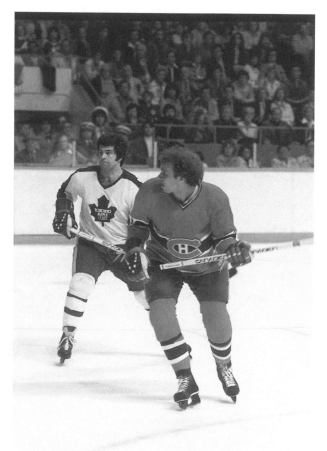

Cam Connor

Mark Napier

61) Tony Esposito
62) Bill Nyrop
63) Mike Polich
64) Mark Napier
65) Cam Connor
66) Pat Hughes
67) Danny Geoffrion
68) Denis Herron
69) Steve Penney
70) Mike McPhee
71) Steve Rooney
72) David Maley
73) Tom Kurvers

Mike Keane

74) Kjell Dahlin

75) Chris Nilan

76) J.J. Daigneault

77) Gilbert Dionne

78) Rob Ramage

79) Mike Keane

80) Doug Gilmour

5

Did You Know?

1) Which Montreal Canadiens star was known by the following nicknames: "The Mitchell Meteor" and "The Babe Ruth of Hockey"?

2) In the early years of the National Hockey League, this general manager was one of its best executives. He won Stanley Cups with Ottawa (1920, '21, '23), Chicago (1934), the Montreal Maroons (1935) and the Canadiens (in 1944 and 1946). Who was he?

3) Two Montreal goaltenders have served as captain of the Canadiens. Can you name them?

4) On February 6, 1943, he scored five goals in a game against Frank Brimsek of the Boston Bruins (in an 8–3 Habs win). He was also known for giving Maurice Richard the nickname "Rocket." He scored 99 goals and 97 assists in 265 games for the Canadiens. Can you name him?

5) Which Montreal Canadien holds the club record for most end-of-season NHL All-Star (first and second team) selections?

Montreal Canadiens stars of the '40s (left to right): Ken Reardon, Bill Durnan and Butch Bouchard.

Dick Irvin coached the Canadiens to three Stanley Cups.

6) Which Montreal coach had the words from John McCrae's well-known poem "In Flanders Fields" inscribed in both French and English on a wall of the Canadiens dressing room? And what are the famous words?

7) The multi-coloured tiers of seats—red, white and blue—that became so much a part of the Montreal Forum's unique history were first implemented by general manager Frank Selke when he took over the team in 1946. He didn't like the drab, dowdy look of the existing stands. What colour were the seats prior to this change?

8) According to the team's media guide, three Montreal Canadiens have worn the number 99 (Leo Bourgeault, Joe Lamb and Des Roche), but only one has worn the number 0 (zero). Who was he?

9) Three Montreal defencemen have worn sweater number 1, a numeral that has traditionally been reserved for goaltenders. Can you name all three blueliners, two of whom are Hall of Fame members?

10) On March 2, 1918, Joe Malone of the Montreal Canadiens scored his 44th goal of the 1917–18 season. That remained the single-season scoring benchmark until February 25, 1944, when another Hab scored his 45th goal of the season. The player in question finished the '44–45 season with an even 50. Who was he, and which goalie gave up the milestone 45th goal?

11) This Montreal netminder is perhaps best known for allowing two overtime goals (1951 to Toronto and 1954 to Detroit) that lost the Stanley Cup for the Canadiens. But he was also in goal when Montreal's Elmer Lach scored an overtime Cup-winner to beat Boston in 1953. Who was the goalie?

12) This goaltender recorded a shutout in his NHL debut against the Montreal Canadiens—the team that owned his rights! The Habs loaned the netminder to Boston on January 14, 1956, and he promptly beat the Canadiens 2–0. He played in only two other NHL games (both with Montreal), but his two brothers (Marcel

Goaltender "Gump" Worsley's given name was Lorne.

and Jean) had much longer NHL careers. Can you name him?

13) This goaltender served as the Boston Bruins' practice goalie for 13 years, but on the night of March 13, 1958, he was loaned to the Canadiens when Jacques Plante was injured during a game. He allowed six goals in a 7–3 Bruins win and never played in another NHL game. Who was he?

14) An October 30, 1963, fight at Maple Leaf Gardens between Toronto's Bob Pulford and this Montreal defenceman continued after both players were escorted into the penalty box. As a result, for the first time in an NHL arena, separate sin bins were installed at the Gardens for each team's wrongdoers. Who was the Habs blueliner?

15) Two players on the Canadiens' 1979 Stanley Cup–winning team were also members of the Edmonton Oilers' 1985 championship squad. Can you name both?

16) As the 1963–64 season began, Gordie Howe was hot on the trail of Maurice Richard's all-time mark of 544 career goals. Ironically, he scored his 544th and 545th goals against the Canadiens during games at the Detroit Olympia. The markers came against two different Habs netminders. Can you name them?

17) May 15, 1964, was an important date in the history of the Canadiens because two significant management changes were announced that day. What two people assumed new roles for the Habs?

18) Only two Montreal team captains have ever scored Stanley Cup–winning goals. Who were they?

19) The first Stanley Cup final game ever played on a Sunday took place at the Montreal Forum. Can you recall the year and the visiting team?

20) He was ridiculed by Toronto Maple Leafs coach Punch Imlach as a "Junior B" goalie during the 1967 Stanley Cup finals, but he went on to play for two Cup winners in

Hockey's greatest general manager, Sam Pollock.

Captain Jean Beliveau decided to play one more year in 1970–71 before retiring.

Montreal (1968 and 1969), then starred for the Los Angeles Kings for a number of years. He also played for Boston and Detroit. Who was he?

21) During the era of the "Original Six" (1942–43 to 1966–67), how many times did the Montreal Canadiens finish in first place?

22) Claude Ruel was young and unknown when he took over for the legendary Toe Blake as coach of the Habs for the 1968–69 season. He won the Stanley Cup that season, but never really seemed to enjoy coaching all that much, even though his overall

record was 172–82–51. How old was he when he guided the Canadiens to the Cup title?

23) This seven-time winner of the Stanley Cup with the Montreal Canadiens went on to play in three Cup finals with the St. Louis Blues (1968 through 1970) and later tried coaching the Blues and the New York Rangers. Who is he?

24) The Canadiens' exhibition game against the Soviets on New Year's Eve 1975 is widely acknowledged as one of the greatest hockey games ever played. The Habs also hosted the Red Army team on December 31,

1979, and won the contest 4–2. Who was in net for Montreal that night?

25) The 1967–68 season saw the debut of rookie Jacques Lemaire, who scored 22 goals and added 20 assists for 42 points in 69 games played. Despite the impressive performance, Lemaire did not win the Calder Trophy. Who won the rookie-of-the-year award in 1968?

26) Montreal legend Jean Beliveau became just the second NHL player (behind Gordie Howe) to record 1,000 career points. He reached the magic number in his 911th

regular-season game by scoring a goal on March 3, 1968. Against which team did Beliveau reach the milestone, and who was the netminder that allowed the goal?

27) This Hall of Fame goaltender earned his first two career shutouts with the Montreal Canadiens during the 1968–69 season. The first came during a 1–0 victory over the Philadelphia Flyers, while the second came in a 0–0 draw against the Boston Bruins on December 21, 1968. The Habs netminder stopped 41 shots, while his counterpart in the Boston net turned away 34 drives before 17,563 fans. Can you name

Defenceman Jean Guy Talbot races to keep the puck out the Montreal goal with Jacques Plante looking on.

the two goalies who each gained a shutout in this standoff?

28) The Montreal Forum underwent major renovations just after the conclusion of the 1968 playoffs. The construction forced the Habs to begin the 1968–69 schedule with eight consecutive road games. They did not play their first home game until November 2, 1968. What was their record over those eight contests? Which team was in town to help the Canadiens reopen the Forum? And what was the final score?

29) The Montreal Canadiens recorded the first-ever NHL draft choice when they selected first overall in the 1963 Amateur Draft. Who did they select?

30) Starting in 1963, the Montreal Canadiens were allowed to draft two French-Canadians before any other team chose a player. The last time they were allowed this privilege was in 1969, when they made the first two choices of the Amateur Draft. Who were the two players selected?

31) During his final season, Jean Beliveau became the fourth NHL player to score 500 career goals. He scored the milestone goal at home against the Minnesota North Stars on February 11, 1971, in his 1,101st career game. Which North Stars netminder gave up the goal?

32) The night of March 20, 1971, proved to be historic when two brothers faced each other in goal for the first time in NHL history. During a game between Montreal and Buffalo at the Forum, Habs starter Rogie Vachon was injured. When the backup netminder took his place, Sabres coach Punch Imlach made a goaltending

Goaltender Rogie Vachon makes a save.

Montreal forward Marc Tardiff looks to score against the Maple Leafs.

change of his own to create the sibling confrontation. Who were the goalies, and who won the game?

33) This former Habs centre, a member of four Stanley Cup–winning Montreal teams, was the first coach of the New York Islanders when they joined the NHL for the 1972–73 season. The native of Lachine, Quebec, lasted 48 games (posting a 6–38–4 record) before he was replaced by Earl Ingarfield. Name him.

34) The Montreal Canadiens were very well represented on the 1972 edition of Team Canada that played the Soviet Union in the

historic Summit Series. A total of six members of the 1972–73 Habs were selected. Can you name them?

35) After edging the Soviet Union in the 1972 series, Team Canada played one more game, against Czechoslovakia, before returning home. Trailing 3–2 late in the game, Canada pulled its goalie in favour of a sixth attacker, and the strategy paid off. Can you name the Montreal Canadien who scored the game-tying goal?

36) On February 17, 1974, during a Sunday-afternoon game against Philadelphia, Flyers tough guy Dave Schultz took a solid beating

from a Montreal defenceman. Who was the Hab who got the better of "The Hammer"?

37) Montreal netminder Ken Dryden faced a team-record 24 shots against in one period of a road game on March 19, 1976. The Habs won 4–1. Who was the opposition?

38) One of the best teams ever assembled was the 1976 edition of Team Canada that won the inaugural Canada Cup tournament. Seven members of the Canadiens were selected to the team. Can you name them?

Bob Gainey is considered one of the best defensive forwards in NHL history.

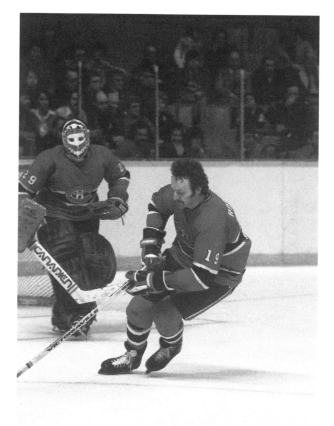

Defenceman Larry Robinson leads the attack for the Canadiens.

39) The 1977 Amateur Draft saw the Montreal Canadiens make a record 27 selections, and 10 of those players chosen appeared in at least one NHL game. Can you name at least five of those who made it to the NHL?

40) Three players selected by the Washington Capitals in the first round of the NHL's Amateur Draft during the 1970s ended up playing for the Montreal Canadiens. Can you name all three?

41) This goaltender was drafted first overall by Montreal in the 1968 Amateur Draft. He was perhaps best known for being the first

Defenceman Chris Chelios was on the Canadiens Stanley Cup team of 1986.

too many men on the ice. The Habs tied the game and won it in overtime. Bruins coach Don Cherry took responsibility for the costly penalty and has never divulged the identity of the extra skater; however, on page 242 of *Offside*, the 1985 book by the longtime hockey writer Stan Fischler, Boston defenceman Mike Milbury fingers the culprit. According to Milbury, which Bruin was the extra man?

43) This singer, as famous for his booming voice as for his renditions of the national anthem

Centre Kirk Muller was acquired by the Canadiens in a deal with the New Jersey Devils and is a native of Kingston, Ontario.

professional netminder ever credited with scoring a goal, when he was playing for the Kansas City Blues of the Central Hockey League in a game on February 21, 1971. He played in a total of 32 games for the Habs, winning 18. He also played in the NHL with St. Louis, Pittsburgh, Kansas City, Colorado and Quebec. Can you name him?

42) The Canadiens were on the verge of elimination during the seventh game of the 1979 semi-finals against the Boston Bruins. They were trailing 4–3 with time running out, when the Bruins were suddenly caught with

Oleg Petrov played in 365 career games for the Canadiens, recording 183 points.

44) The first expansion club to record a playoff victory against an established NHL team beat the Canadiens 6–3 on Forum ice on April 22, 1971. Another expansion club won its first playoff game ever when it beat the Habs 2–1 on April 15, 1975. Can you name these teams?

45) The record for the fastest goal to start a playoff game is six seconds, set by the Los Angeles Kings on April 17, 1977. Less than one month later, on May 5, this Montreal player scored a goal just seven seconds into a playoff

Pierre Turgeon was the captain of the Canadiens when they played their last game at the Montreal Forum.

before Canadiens home games, raised eyebrows when he changed the lyrics to "O Canada" to include the phrase "for rights and liberty" as issues Canadians stand on guard for. Who was this rather courageous crooner?

game on the road. Who scored the goal, and where were the Canadiens playing that night?

46) The Winnipeg Jets had the first selection in the 1979 expansion draft, and they claimed a player from the Montreal Canadiens' list of available talent. Although they owned his NHL rights, this player had not participated in a single game as a Hab. In the Jets' first year of NHL action, he scored a respectable 18 goals in 57 games. He also went on to play for the Chicago Blackhawks. Who was he?

47) Against which teams did the following Montreal legends score their first career goal: Howie Morenz, Maurice Richard, Jean Beliveau and Guy Lafleur?

48) This Winnipeg-born defenceman was the NHL's plus/minus leader in 1980–81 (at plus-63) and was named to the league's second All-Star team in 1982 before he was dealt away to the Washington Capitals. Can you name him?

49) April 20, 1984, was Good Friday, but that night at the Forum, the Montreal Canadiens and Quebec Nordiques staged one of the wildest brawls in the history of playoff hockey. The teams combined for 252 penalty minutes in Montreal's 5–3 win, which eliminated Quebec. Things got so bad that a flare-up delayed the start of the third period! One Montreal player was seriously hurt when the Nords' Louis Sleigher sucker-punched him in the eye. Who was the injured Montreal player?

50) The Canadiens had one of their very best entry drafts in 1984—their first four

Vincent Damphousse has been a consistent point producer everywhere he has played.

selections all made major contributions to the team and had long NHL careers. All four also played with other NHL teams before their playing days were over. Can you name them?

51) On January 12, 1985, the Montreal Canadiens introduced their 75th anniversary All-Star team. Can you name the coach, goaltender, two defencemen and three forwards selected for this prestigious group?

52) Four Montreal Canadiens coaches have won the Stanley Cup in their first year behind an NHL bench. Can you name all four, and the years in which they took the Cup?

53) Which NHL team was the first to record 5,000 points, and when did it happen?

54) Although he did not win player-of-the-game honours (that distinction went to Mario Lemieux of Pittsburgh), this Canadien set a record with five assists during the 1988 All-Star Game in St. Louis, helping the Wales Conference to a 6–5 overtime win over the Campbell Conference. Can you name him?

55) The 1988 Winter Olympics were held in Calgary, Alberta, and each of the Canadian-based NHL teams tried to help out Team Canada by loaning the national squad a player off their roster. Which Hab did the Canadiens send?

56) This goaltender from Toronto played in only one game for the Canadiens—for three minutes, to be exact. His chance came when Patrick Roy had to go to the bathroom during a January 27, 1989, contest! He played in only one other NHL game, for Edmonton, after his time with the Habs. Can you name him?

57) The Montreal Canadiens won the Stanley Cup at the Montreal Forum on 15 different occasions. Meanwhile, only one visiting team ever won the Cup on Forum ice. It happened on May 25, 1989, when the Habs were defeated 4–2 in the sixth game of the finals. Which team pulled off the feat?

58) Montreal has traditionally allowed its players to vote for the captain of the team. The ballot conducted before the 1989–90 season had an unusual result in that two players ended up earning the same number of votes. It was therefore decided that the two would share the captaincy for the season. Who were the co-captains?

59) Who are the only two men to coach both the Toronto Maple Leafs and the Montreal Canadiens?

Goaltender Andy Moog played his last NHL season with the Canadiens.

Defenceman Rod Langway (standing behind Mario Tremblay) was a part of the Canadiens Stanley Cup team of 1979.

60) Since 1986, the NHL has presented the team that posts the best regular-season record with the Presidents' Trophy. How many times have the Canadiens won this award?

61) Which Montreal team trainer has his name on the Stanley Cup a total of 10 times?

62) When the Ottawa Senators re-entered the NHL in 1992–93, they played their first game against the Canadiens at home. Who won the contest?

63) En route to winning the Stanley Cup in 1993, the Montreal Canadiens played in 11 overtime playoff games. They lost the first one, to the Quebec Nordiques, then took the next 10 in a row to establish a record that may never be broken. Who scored the game-winner for the Nordiques, and which players scored the winners for the Habs (there are seven different Montreal players to be named)?

64) A member of the NHL's All-Rookie Team after his 12-goal, 27-point season in 1993–94, this Russian right winger spent parts of eight

Montreal's Guy Carbonneau tries to get around Toronto defenceman Jim Benning.

Forward Richard Zednik scored 26 goals for the Canadiens in 2003–04.

for the Habs in the same game. Can you name him?

66) On December 2, 1995, the Montreal Canadiens suffered one of the worst defeats in team history when Detroit beat them 11–1. (Through the end of the 2003–04 season, the Habs have allowed 11 goals in a game only six times.) What else happened to make that loss to the Red Wings even more regrettable?

67) A three-time Stanley Cup–winning goalie with the Edmonton Oilers (in 1984, '85 and '87), this netminder had also played very well for the Boston Bruins and Dallas Stars before the Canadiens signed him as a free agent in July of 1997 for his last NHL season. Who was he?

68) A six-foot, 195-pound centre from Pont-Rouge, Quebec, led all scorers during the 1992 Winter Olympics when he racked up 15 points in eight games for Team Canada. He had a 102-point season for Boston in 1992–93 and also played for Washington, Buffalo, Ottawa and Phoenix before being traded to the Canadiens in 2001. He played three seasons for the Habs before retiring in May of 2004. Can you name him?

seasons with the Canadiens before he was dealt to the Nashville Predators in March of 2003. Can you name him?

65) A new regime of Rejean Houle (general manager) and Mario Tremblay (coach) was announced before a Saturday-night game against the Toronto Maple Leafs on October 21, 1995. The Montreal Canadiens won the game 4–3 on a goal scored at 19:59 of the third period. Who scored the goal? Also, another player scored his only career goal

69) Since the 1998–99 season the NHL has awarded the Maurice "Rocket" Richard Trophy to the player who scores the most goals during the regular season. The trophy was donated to the league to honour the first player to score 50 goals in one year, a star who led the NHL in goals five times in his career. Who was the first winner of the award, and how many goals did he score that season?

70) Although he had just recently been acquired, this right winger scored the 10,000th home-ice goal for the Canadiens (in 2,675 games) during a 3–1 win over San Jose on January 27, 2002. The Canadiens were the first team in NHL history to score that many goals at home. Who was the player who scored the goal?

71) True or false: the Montreal Canadiens have missed the playoffs in three straight seasons on two occasions.

72) Five NHL teams have retired or honoured the sweater numbers of former Montreal Canadiens. Can you name the teams and the players?
Note: One of the teams has retired two numbers.

73) Montreal right winger Michael Ryder led all rookies in assists (38) and points (63) during the 2003–04 season, yet he did not win the Calder Trophy. Which goaltender took the rookie-of-the-year award that season?

74) Of the five players listed as having played in the most career playoff games (as of the end of the 2003–04 season), four were members of the Montreal Canadiens at one point in their careers. Can you name them?

75) One of the greatest events in hockey history took place on November 22, 2003, when 57,167 fans watched the Montreal Canadiens and Edmonton Oilers play a regular-season game outdoors at Edmonton's Commonwealth Stadium in what was billed as the Heritage Classic. Who won the contest, and which player scored the winning goal?

76) The Montreal Canadiens have retired seven sweater numbers in recognition of the outstanding service rendered by seven different players. Can you name the players and their numbers?

77) How many times have the Montreal Canadiens been on the losing end of a four-game sweep in a best-of-seven playoff series?

78) The first captains of the Pittsburgh Penguins (1967–68), Florida Panthers (1993–94) and

Defenceman Craig Rivet (#52) was drafted 68th overall by the Canadiens in 1992.

Columbus Blue Jackets (2000–01) were all former Montreal Canadiens players. Can you name all three?

79) The first men to coach the Oakland Seals (1967–68), Atlanta Flames (1972–73) and Minnesota Wild (2000–01) were all former players with the Montreal Canadiens. Who were they?

80) In 2003–04, the Montreal Canadiens had 12 players (who appeared in at least 10 regular-season games over the course of the season) who wore sweater numbers above 40. Can you name at least five of them?

After 554 career games as a Hab, defenceman Terry Harper was dealt to the Los Angeles Kings.

Howie Morenz wore sweater number seven for the Canadiens.

81) In a surprise move during the 2005 Entry Draft, the Canadiens selected a goaltender with the fifth pick overall. Name him and the junior team he played for.

82) With the new collective agreement in place for the 2005–06 season, the Montreal Canadiens were able to participate in the free agency period that began August 1, 2005. The first two free agents signed by the team were players that had been on Stanley Cup–winning teams. Name both.

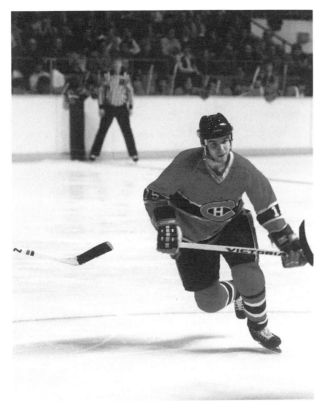

Rejean Houle was named general manager of the Canadiens in 1995.

Answers

1) Howie Morenz
2) Tommy Gorman
3) George Hainsworth (for the 1932–33 season) and Bill Durnan (for part of the 1947–48 season, after captain "Toe" Blake suffered a broken leg)
4) Ray Getliffe
5) Maurice Richard was an NHL All-Star 15 times (eight times on the first team, seven times on the second team).
6) Dick Irvin had the following words from the poem put on the dressing-room wall: "To you from failing hands we throw the torch; be yours to hold it high."
7) Brown
8) Goaltender Paul Bibeault wore zero during the 1942–43 season.

9) Herb Gardiner, Babe Siebert and Marty Burke all wore number 1 while playing defence. Tony Graboski (a Hab between 1940–1943) also wore number 1, but he is listed as a left wing/defenceman in the record books.
10) Maurice Richard broke Malone's record against goaltender Frank McCool of the Toronto Maple Leafs.
11) Gerry McNeil
12) Claude Pronovost
13) Don Aiken
14) Terry Harper
15) Mark Napier and Pat Hughes
16) Gump Worsley and Charlie Hodge
17) David Molson became president of the team and Sam Pollock was named general manager.

Ken Dryden retired from the Canadiens after winning the Stanley Cup in 1979.

Guy Lafleur retired from the Canadiens in 1984 but returned to play for the New York Rangers and Quebec Nordiques.

18) Toe Blake (1944 and 1946) and Jean Beliveau (1965)

19) On April 24, 1966, the Detroit Red Wings defeated the Canadiens 3–2 in the first game of the Stanley Cup finals.

20) Rogie Vachon

21) Twelve times

22) Claude Ruel was 30 years old when the Canadiens won the Stanley Cup in 1969.

23) Jean-Guy Talbot

24) Richard Sevigny

25) Derck Sanderson of the Boston Bruins, who had 24 goals and 49 points.

26) Roger Crozier of the Detroit Red Wings allowed the goal during a 5–2 win over the Canadiens.

27) Tony Esposito was in the Montreal net, while Gerry Cheevers defended the Boston goal.

28) The Canadiens went 6–1–1 to start the '68–69 season. Montreal defeated Detroit 2–1 in the first game at the refurbished Forum.

29) Garry Monahan

30) Rejean Houle and Marc Tardif

31) Gilles Gilbert

32) Ken Dryden of the Canadiens won the game 5–2 over older brother Dave Dryden of the Sabres. Dave had started the contest for Buffalo, but had been replaced after the first whistle.

33) Phil Goyette

In addition to Montreal, defenceman Brian Engblom also played for Washington, Los Angeles, Buffalo and Calgary during his NHL career.

34) Ken Dryden, Serge Savard, Guy Lapointe, Frank and Peter Mahovlich and Yvan Cournoyer

35) Serge Savard

36) Larry Robinson

37) The California Golden Seals

38) Guy Lafleur, Steve Shutt, Bob Gainey, Larry Robinson, Guy Lapointe, Peter Mahovlich and Serge Savard

39) Gordie Roberts (1,097 career games), Rod Langway (994), Mark Napier (767), Craig Laughlin (549), Norm Dupont (256), Richard Sevigny (176), Robbie Holland (44), Mark Holden (8), Daniel Poulin (3) and Moe Robinson (1)

Patrick Roy holds the NHL career record for most wins by a goaltender—551.

Joe Juneau's (#50) best season in Montreal saw him record 36 points in 70 games during 2001–02.

40) Rick Green (first overall in 1976), Robert Picard (third overall in 1977) and Ryan Walter (second overall in 1978)

41) Michel Plasse

42) Stan Jonathan

43) Roger Doucet

44) The Minnesota North Stars (1971) and the Vancouver Canucks (1975)

45) Bob Gainey scored the goal against the New York Islanders.

46) Peter Marsh

47) Morenz scored against the Ottawa Senators on December 26, 1923; Richard against the New York Rangers on November 8, 1942; Beliveau against the

Defenceman Lyle Odelein scored a career-high 11 goals for Montreal in 1993–94.

Chicago Blackhawks on January 27, 1951; and Lafleur against the Los Angeles Kings on October 23, 1971.

48) Brian Engblom

49) Jean Hamel

50) Petr Svoboda, Shayne Corson, Stephane Richer and Patrick Roy

51) Toe Blake, coach; Jacques Plante, goaltender; Larry Robinson and Doug Harvey, defencemen; Maurice Richard, Jean Beliveau and Dickie Moore, forwards.

52) Toe Blake (1956), Claude Ruel (1969), Al MacNeil (1971) and Jean Perron (1986)

53) Montreal hit the 5,000-point mark by beating Winnipeg 5–3 on October 18, 1986.

54) Mats Naslund

55) Serge Boisvert

56) Randy Exelby

57) The Calgary Flames

58) Guy Carbonneau and Chris Chelios

59) Dick Irvin and Pat Burns

60) None. They were the runners-up twice, in 1987–88 and 1988–89.

61) Eddy Palchak. The last time his name was engraved on the Stanley Cup, it was as the equipment manager.

62) Ottawa beat Montreal 5–3.

63) Scott Young scored for the Nordiques. John LeClair (two), Guy Carbonneau (two), Kirk Muller (two), Gilbert Dionne, Vincent Damphousse, Stephane Lebeau and Eric Desjardins scored in overtime for the Canadiens.

64) Oleg Petrov

65) Pierre Turgeon scored the last-second game-winning goal, while Craig Ferguson recorded the only marker of his tenure with the Canadiens.

66) Goaltender Patrick Roy, humiliated at being left in the Canadiens net for nine goals before he was replaced, told Canadiens president Ronald Corey that he had played his last game as a Hab. The exchange was captured by television cameras and beamed across the country on *Hockey Night in Canada*.

67) Andy Moog

68) Joe Juneau

69) Teemu Selanne scored 47 goals.

70) Sergei Berezin

71) True. The first such run took place in 1920, '21 and '22. The second post-season drought was in 1999, 2000 and 2001.

72) The Quebec Nordiques (who have since moved to Colorado) retired J.C. Tremblay's number 3 (for his contribution when the team was in the World Hockey Association) and Marc Tardif's number 8. The Chicago Blackhawks have retired Tony Esposito's number 35. Another ex-Montreal goalie, Rogie Vachon, had his number 30 retired by the Los

Angeles Kings. And Rod Langway's number 5 was retired by the Washington Capitals. Meanwhile, the Toronto Maple Leafs have declared Frank Mahovlich's number 27 as one of its "honoured numbers."

73) Andrew Raycroft of the Boston Bruins

74) Patrick Roy (240 career playoff games), Claude Lemieux (233), Guy Carbonneau (231) and Larry Robinson (227). Mark Messier, who ranks second on the list with 236 post-season appearances, is the only player in the top five who has never played for Montreal.

75) Montreal won the game 4–3. Richard Zednik scored the winner.

76) Jacques Plante (1), Doug Harvey (2), Jean Beliveau (4), Howie Morenz (7), Maurice Richard (9), Guy Lafleur (10) and Henri Richard (16)

77) Four times: in 2004 (vs. Tampa Bay), 1998 (Buffalo), 1992 (Boston) and 1952 (Detroit)

78) Ab McDonald was the first to wear the "C" for Pittsburgh. Brian Skrudland was Florida's first captain. And Lyle Odelein was the captain of the Blue Jackets in their inaugural season.

79) The three coaches were Bert Olmstead (Oakland), Bernie Geoffrion (Atlanta) and Jacques Lemaire (Minnesota).

80) The high numbers were worn by Patrice Brisebois (43), Sheldon Souray (44), Francis Bouillion (51), Craig Rivet (52), Jose Theodore (60), Ron Hainsey (65), Mike Ribeiro (71), Michael Ryder (73), Andrei Markov (79), Marcel Hossa (81), Joe Juneau (90) and Yanic Perreault (94).

81) Carey Price of the Tri-City Americans (WHL)

82) Alexei Kovalev (a member of the Habs in 2003–04 and a Cup winner with New York in 1994) and Mathieu Dandenault (a three-time Cup winner with Detroit)

Sheldon Souray (#44) had 15 goals and 35 points for the Canadiens in 2003–04.

Maurice Richard finished his great career with 544 regular season goals.

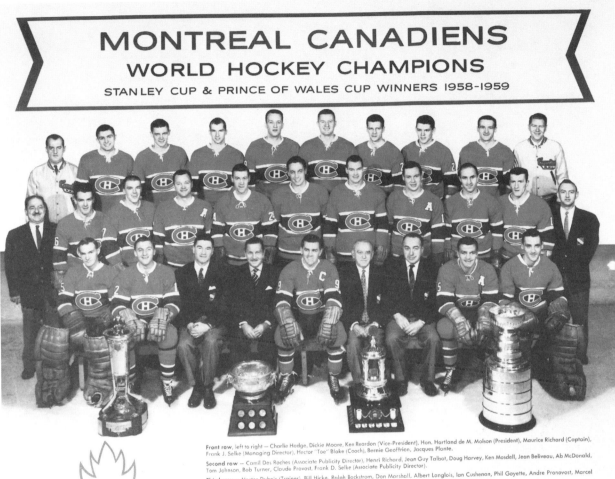

MONTREAL CANADIENS
WORLD HOCKEY CHAMPIONS
STANLEY CUP & PRINCE OF WALES CUP WINNERS 1958-1959

Front row, left to right — Charlie Hodge, Dickie Moore, Ken Reardon (Vice-President), Hon. Hartland de M. Molson (President), Maurice Richard (Captain), Frank J. Selke (Managing Director), Hector "Toe" Blake (Coach), Bernie Geoffrion, Jacques Plante.

Second row — Camil Des Roches (Associate Publicity Director), Henri Richard, Jean Guy Talbot, Doug Harvey, Ken Mosdell, Jean Beliveau, Ab McDonald, Tom Johnson, Bob Turner, Claude Provost, Frank D. Selke (Associate Publicity Director).

Third row — Hector Dubois (Trainer), Bill Hicke, Ralph Backstrom, Don Marshall, Albert Langlois, Ian Cushenan, Phil Goyette, Andre Pronovost, Marcel Bonin, Larry Aubut (Assistant Trainer).

The 1958–59 incarnation of the Montreal Canadiens is considered one of the best of all time.